Delving in Dinorwig

Douglas C. Carrington

GWASG Carreg Gwalch

ISBN: 0-86381-285-6

First published in 1994 by Gwasg Carreg Gwalch,
Iard yr Orsaf, Llanrwst, Gwynedd, Wales.

☎ 0492 642031

Printed and published in Wales

Douglas Corlett Carrington, a retired chartered chemist and chemical engineer, spent nearly the whole of his working life in power stations. An interest in slate quarry locomotives, over twenty five years ago, developed into an interest in the whole slate quarrying process, particularly at Dinorwig. He has written previously on the topic. He has also been involved in the preservation of one of the Dinorwig steam locomotives.

Being a half Manxman, the author also has an interest in the relationship between the Celtic nations.

Contents

Front cover:
Bernstein pauses at "New York" during the descent from
Pen Garret to lake level

Preface

This book has been in the making for nearly five years; though the interest began nearly thirty years ago. The author certainly did not realise that it would become such an absorbing interest when he made his first visit to Dinorwig Slate Quarry, all those years ago. The site was, indeed still is, a remarkable place. It is now an underground, pumped storage, hydro-electric power station of world class status; although the remains of the quarry still dominate the site.

It must be stressed at the outset, that although the book deals with now historical topics, it is by no means a history. A historian must seek to examine all aspects of his subject. The author has not subjected himself to such a discipline; he has only written about the things that have interested him, during the many years, since that first visit.

One of the pleasing aspects of the thirty years is the number of similarly interested people; some of whom the author is grateful to include among his friends. Slate quarrying is still carried on in Wales, but all quarrying at Dinorwig ceased in 1969. Nevertheless, any mention of it still evokes a feeling of pride in local people. It still remains a very Welsh and personal thing, so much so, that without the help, understanding and interest of local people, any description of the quarry could be a cold and soulless thing.

The author received much willing help from both the late "Tommy" Morris, the quarry chief engineer and his successor Hugh Richard Jones. The help and encouragement received from these gentlemen is greatly appreciated. Conversations and correspondence with the Rev. Herbert Thomas of Llanor, whose ancestors were long associated with the quarry management, have given an invaluable glimpse into early planning ideas. Sooner or later, the student of a topic as Welsh as slate quarrying, will come up against the language. Guidance with the language and the general topic has come from the author's good friend, Hugh Arthur Jones. He has read the various drafts and his constructive comments have been invaluable. The same comment applies to Emyr Jones, whose book on the quarry and its workers, *Bargen Dinorwig*, won a First Prize at the 1979 National Eisteddfod. Thanks are also due to Paul Towers for reading the draft and for advice on publication. Although the author's good friend and co-author of *Slates to Velinheli*, Tom Rushworth, died some years ago, his influence can still be discerned in this book. The author is indebted to his friend John B. Firth for the use of negatives for some of the photographs in Chapter 15.

Anybody who writes about a Welsh Slate quarry will, sooner or later, find himself at Gwynedd Archives Service, Caernarfon Office. The writer can only repeat the praise of other writers, for the staff at that office. They have a genuine interest in their visitors' work and nothing is too much trouble for them. I should particularly like to thank M/s Anne Venables, now Archivist at the Llangefni office.

Over the years the author has had discussions and correspondence with other interested people. These include George Barnes, Emlyn Baylis, James Boyd, Vic Bradley, Tony Coultiss, Thomas Evans (Clwb y Bont), William Jones (son of Richard Jones, M.M.s driver), Andrew McDougall, Dr Dafydd Roberts (Welsh Slate Museum, Llanberis), Tomos Roberts, (Archivist UCNW), the late Gordon Ward. A "thankyou" is given to all for their help and interest. If any person has been omitted would they please accept the author's apologies.

Finally, I must thank my wife Jean. She has been all important in this project, she has climbed up the quarry, she has sat in the car for hours while I climbed up the quarry. There is no cafe at the top of Dinorwig, but I never went hungry. She has entertained my friends. She has typed and checked my typing. I can only say, a very big thankyou.

Foreword

When the last slate was quarried at Dinorwig in July 1969, a few days after the investiture of Prince Charles at Caernarfon Castle, a line was drawn under the history of an industry that had flourished on the slopes of Elidir Fawr for almost two hundred years. What had initially been little more than a series of scratchings above Llyn Padarn and Llyn Peris, extending towards Allt Ddu, grew to be one of the two largest slate quarries in the world, employing by the mid nineteenth century a labour force of over 3000 men, and producing around 100,000 tons of roofing slates annually.

Its technology was, at that time, second to none. Sophisticated railway and tramway networks carried the slates through the quarry and down to the coast at Y Felinheli, where a first rate port and standard gauge rail interchange was provided to take Dinorwig slate to its markets in the United Kingdom, Europe and worldwide. An engineering works at Gilfach Ddu replaced, in 1870, earlier facilities on Ffeiar Injan gallery, and enabled the quarry to become largely self-sufficient in terms of its ability to repair and maintain anything from a wagon coupling to a steam locomotive. Dinorwig Quarry hospital provided the services of skilled and innovative surgeons to minister to the needs of those who had injured themselves at work in the quarry. There was no lack of demand.

But the quarry was repsonsible for more than just a series of technological and logistical superlatives. In its shadow grew a network of interlinked industrial villages, developing in areas which had hitherto been depopulated agricultural communities. Llanberis, Deiniolen, Llanrug, Bethel, Cwm-y-Glo: all these, and many more, grew to house and serve the quarrymen whose bargain for life was at Dinorwig. In their chapels and vestry halls, their taverns and football fields, men and women worshipped and sang, argued and played, creating a vibrant self-conscious industrial community that was proud of itself and its craft skills. Here, too, in 1874, the North Wales Quarrymens Union took root and flourished, while authors like T. Rowland Hughes found inspiration in the interaction of members of the community.

Douglas Carrington describes here the focus for all of this. "Y Chwaral" was central to all that happened, and this author's interest in its activity, combined with his eye for detail, provides a wealth of fascinating information.

Dafydd Roberts
The Welsh Slate Museum, Llanberis
May 1994

1. Maps, Plans and Aerial Photographs

During the compilation of this series of essays on transport and allied topics, in and around Dinorwig Slate Quarry, the author soon came to realise how dependent he was on the available maps of the district. During nearly 200 years of quarrying, massive destructive changes occured in the geography of the site. The destruction was double-edged, first the actual excavations continually removed geographical reference points and second, the colossal volumes of slate waste, as much as nine times that of saleable product, obliterated other sites. It seems to the author, that an important consideration is that although the quarrying was along a horizontal "front", and the geographical co-ordinates of a site might change; the name and altitude would remain the same.

Bearing in mind the above comments, it is useful to assess the reliability of the various maps used in the following chapters. The first "sketch" of real significance was surveyed by R. Lloyd Ellis of "Carnarvon" in 1836[1]. The map is 27 inches (686mm) long by 19 inches (483mm) wide, but following the passage of time, it is not too clear. However, it has been re-traced and a reduction to a page size is appended. Illus.1. Because of the destruction in the quarry, the author has used incline sites as a "scaling tool" to determine the altitude of intermediate locations. This procedure is only acceptable if the scale of the map is known with reasonable accuracy. It can be assessed by comparing the relative position of sites on the map with the same sites on a modern map of proven accuracy. As far as the Ellis map is concerned, the author has only been able to locate four static sites, on both the map and the first edition of the "25 inch" plan, published by the Ordnance Survey in 1889. There are two dimensioned "fields" but unfortunately, they cannot be identified on later maps. In the table below, a number of dimensions on the Ellis map have been quantified by comparison with the 1886 Ordnance Survey "25 inch" plan.

Dimension	Length-25″	O.S.feet	Ellis-″	Ellis-ft/″	A4-ft/″
AB	17.75	3749	7.00	536	1041
CB	21.75	4488	8.00	561	1069
EB	10.75	2270	7.00	324	631
CA	4.75	1003	2.75	365	716
AE	12.00	2534	4.50	563	1056

It will be seen that the scale of the map is by no means constant; the A4 scale varying from 1,069 feet/inch in a north-west direction to 631 feet per inch in a north-east direction. For what it is worth the mean A4 scale is 900 feet/inch or 5.8 inches/miles. Although apparently similar in scale to a modern "six inch" map, it can be shown that it would be statistically unsound to compare the map with a modern one. The main value of the Ellis map is that it names 17 quarry sites and their relative locations. In addition, the incline and limited track positions are valuable information.

In 1841, the Ordnance Survey published the First Edition of the "One Inch" map of the district, Sheet No.78 and in 1970 it was republished by David and Charles, Sheet No.24. In 1964, J.B. Harley wrote that although the "One Inch" map was the least reliable of those produced by the Survey, they were a great improvement on contemporary privately produced maps[2]. Perhaps this is borne out by the scale anomalies of the Ellis map. He also states that the time between surveying and publishing, could be as long as twenty years. The clarity of the map is not ideal; slope is indicated by the "hachure" method and the printing plates are rather worn. The full length of the Dinorwig Railway is shown and labelled "Rail-road". In order to check the scale of the map, a transparent Xerox copy, enlarged to a six inch (152mm) scale, has been prepared. On overlaying this on a modern six inch edition, it is clear that there is a good match of scale and non-quarry features. The enlarged Survey map shows a superficial similarity of shape and scale to the page size Ellis map. In addition, there is also a tramway or road, from what are probably the Allt Ddu and Bryn Glas quarries, to what could be an incline on an equivalent site to the later Chwarel Fawr incline.

During the next forty years, the improvement in the quality of the Survey is striking, particularly the first edition of the twenty five inch plans of the district, which were published in 1886. In his investigations the author has used these maps extensively. Unlike the current maps which are based on a coherent National Grid system; the older maps and plans, the *County* series, were based on counties. They are of very high

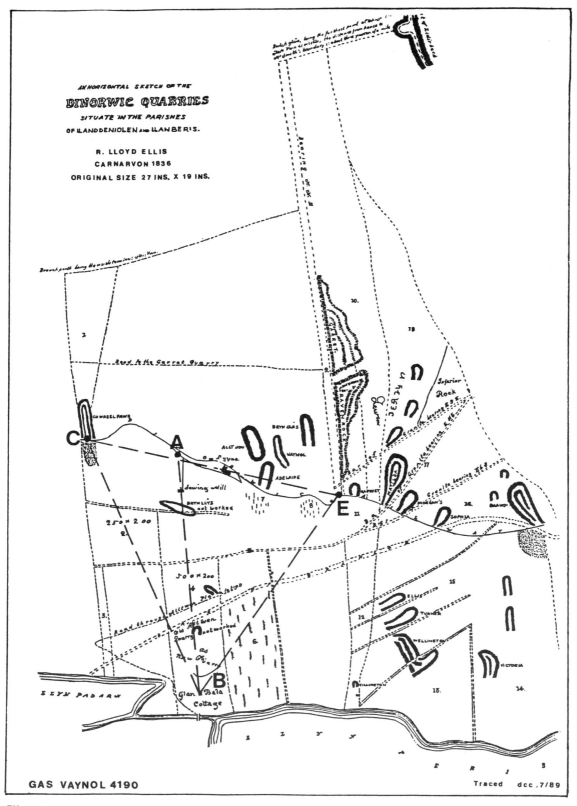

An Horizontal Sketch of the

DINORWIC QUARRIES

SITUATE IN THE PARISHES
OF LLANDDENIOLEN AND LLANBERIS.

R. LLOYD ELLIS
CARNARVON 1836
ORIGINAL SIZE 27 INS. X 19 INS.

GAS VAYNOL 4190

Traced   dcc.7/89

Illus.1

FROM THE FIRST EDITION OF
THE ONE INCH ORDNANCE
SURVEY OF ENGLAND & WALES

ORIGINAL SHEET NO. 78.
FIRST PUBLISHED 9/1841
D. & C. SHEET NO. 24.

1,000 YARDS

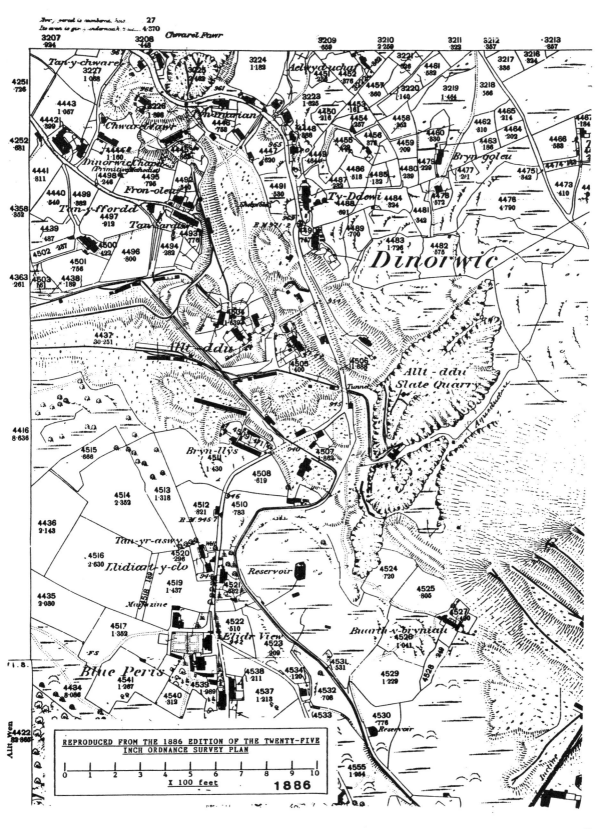

REPRODUCED FROM THE 1886 EDITION OF THE TWENTY-FIVE
INCH ORDNANCE SURVEY PLAN

0 1 2 3 4 5 6 7 8 9 10

X 100 feet

1886

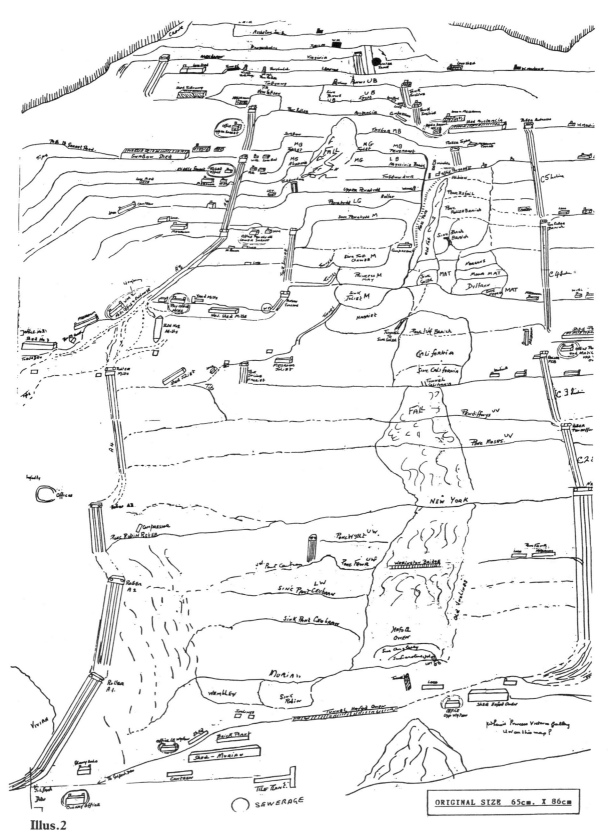

Illus.2

quality, both content and preparation; and can stand comparison with later sheets produced by modern technology. The referencing system, using both Roman and Arabic numerals, can be confusing and anomalous. For example, the Port Dinorwig sheet shows both Anglesey and Carnarfonshire referencing.

The standard sheet measured 38″ x 25 ⅓″, but quarter sheets were also available. A "Six Inch" map was also published but this was rather congested. In fact, it was a photo reduction of the "25 inch" version. In addition, there are the various editions of the "2½ inch" and "One inch" maps, but these are only suitable for general use.

Some years ago, the author was given a copy of an anonymous sketch of the quarry[3] (Illus.2). Although not drawn by a professional surveyor, it is a very valuable relic. The author believes it was drawn by the clerk in the Gilfach Ddu office. It illustrates in an attractive plan cum elevation style, the names of numerous locations in the quarry. The diagram is not scaled and dated, but as the brick and tile plants are shown, it must be of relatively recent origin. The original of the document is now held by Gwynedd Archives. Other maps used by the author will be described in the relevant parts of the text.

Another valuable source of information is aerial photography. In April 1954, the Royal Air Force flew a number of sorties over the quarry and took a number of vertical photographs. These were taken on a clear sunny day. The prints measure 8¼″ x 7″ (210mm x 178mm) with a scale of seven inches per mile. As for resolution at this scale, the four feet (1.22m) gauge Padarn Railway lines can be distinguished with the help of a small lens. A 1′ 10¾″ (578mm) gauge engine can be seen taking water at Gilfach Ddu. JERRY M was in service on the tramway at the time. Incidentally, photographs of Penrhyn Quarry were taken at the same time. Another source of aerial photographs are the Cambridge University selections taken in 1948, 1949 and 1963. These are oblique photographs of varying scale; some of which are of excellent quality and content. Messrs. Airviews Ltd. have also taken first class photographs, some of them in colour. When the Central Electricity Generating Board were planning Dinorwig Power Station, they commissioned a selection of aerial photographs, both vertical and oblique. The trouble with aerial photographs is that they are expensive. A further source of photographic information must be mentioned, the excellent collection in the custody of Gwynedd Archives Service, Caernarfon.

The reader might have wondered, what is a map and what is a plan? As far the Ordnance Survey is concerned, a "map" has a scale up to twenty-five inches per mile and a "plan" has a scale bigger than this. i.e. 25+ inches per mile.

In this series of essays, all Ordnance Survey map references refer to the one hundred kilometre square, "SH". Only the co-ordinates are quoted; these have an accuracy of +/− 100 metres.

Relevant Imperial = SI Conversions
      1 mile = 1.609 kilometres.
      1 yard = 0.914 metres.
      1 foot = 305 mm.
      1 inch = 25.4 mm.

S.I. equivalents are quoted in parentheses adjacent to Imperial units. However, in places the conversion to S.I. units can be somewhat inapt in quarry terms. The percentage system of defining gradient is quoted alongside the traditional British (1 in x) system.

Note
Reduced scale examples of the 1886 and 1914 25″ Ordnance Survey maps are included between Chapters 6 and 7.

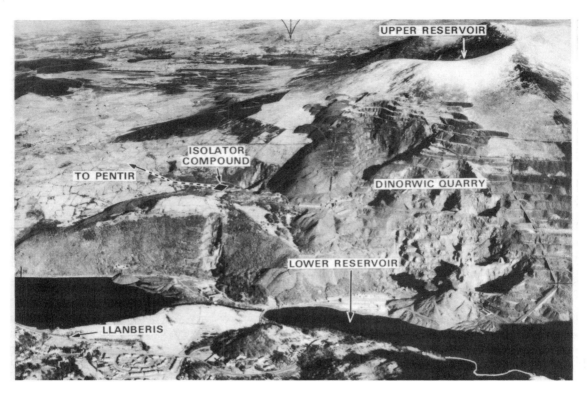

Dinorwig scheme — aerial view looking north

Dinorwig Quarry in the 1850's — from Reminiscences of the life of the late Sir Thomas Assheton Smith,
Sir J. E. Eardley Wilmot 2nd Edition, 1860

2. Setting the Scene

The Allt Ddu district, one mile north-east of Llanberis, is the site of the beginnings of a commercial exploitation of slate that culminated in the massive Dinorwig Slate Quarry. The name Dinorwig comes from Llys Dinorwig (*Dinorwig Court*), an ancient site (561631), some two miles north-west of Dinorwig village. Before the area was "landscaped" in the mid 1980's, the observer was confronted with a seemingly ruinous industrial chaos. However, until the vandals and scrap dealers had done their worst, Allt Ddu (*black hillside*) and the associated Chwarel Fawr (*big quarry*) were examples of the massive and ingenious engineering works that were gouged out of the spectacular scenery.

When considering an old slate quarry site, it cannot be over-stressed that colossal tonnages of rock were involved and that as little as one ninth was to become a saleable product; the remainder had to be removed and disposed of. It might seem obvious, but to reduce transport costs to a minimum, all movements should be downward or at least horizontal. Any upward movement would have required some form of expensive powered transport to be provided. Allt Ddu was a paradox; in that all prepared slate went uphill and the waste remained on the level or went downhill; despite the fact that a downhill route for the whole lot was feasible. This contradiction has been and still is, the reason for a number of puzzles and anomalies in the area.

It is not the author's purpose to describe in detail the early history of the area; this has already been dealt with by Lindsay[4] and Boyd[5]. However, it might be helpful to give a minimum account in order to set the scene. The land thereabout was owned by the Assheton Smith family of Parc y Faenol (*Vaynol Park*), an estate on the mainland shore of the Menai Straits. Slate quarrying on their land was originally carried out on an ad hoc basis by local farmer/quarriers, who paid an annual or "take-note"[6] fee of one guinea to the lord of the manor. (Was a "take-note" an authority to extract slate or was it a notice or instruction?) At this time, the 18th century, North Wales was remote from English markets and with roads unsuitable for intensive usage. It was necessary for the prepared slate to be carried, some eight miles (12.9km) to Caernarfon or Moel y Don, the nearest ports for shipment to England and Ireland. One route was overland by packhorse to Moel y Don, later Port Dinorwig. The other route was tedious, necessitating three trans-shipments. The first stage was by packhorse or cart to the top of the steep Allt Wen (*white hillside*) which overlooked Llyn Padarn, along which the slate was to be ferried. The brow of the hill was about 600 feet (183m) above the lake and movement of slate down the hillside was a major impediment. The way was steep and the slate had to be dragged on a sledge, braked at the rear by a slate block; which was presumably split at the lake-side in to a saleable product. It was a hazardous procedure, with the disadvantage that the sledge had to be dragged back up the hill. Nevertheless, it is remarkable that in 1787-8 nearly half a million slates were lowered to Cei Newydd (*new quay*). It had already become a major enterprise. Slate was also taken down to Y Cei (*the quay*) on Llyn Peris, which was joined to Llyn Padarn by the then navigable Afon y Bala. The slates were shipped along the lake to Penllyn (*lake end*) or a little further along the Afon (*river*) Rhythallt to Cwm y Glo (*coal valley*). This transport is described in detail by Ilsley[7]. The journey to the port was completed by horse and cart, to the serious detriment of the roads.

In 1787 Assheton Smith, with a view to a profitable expansion, evicted the ad hoc operators and let the rights to a partnership of three, William Bridge, Hugh Ellis and Thomas Wright; who were already operating a copper mine on the Great Orme[8]. They had plans for an operation on a much bigger scale than previously, and during 1788 work was started on the "Great New Quarry" on the slopes above Llyn Peris. The partners were under no illusions about the difficulties in getting the slate to the coast, and on reading their correspondence, one can sense the near panic as efforts were made to expedite deliveries. Two main routes had already been established, but both had the problem of the 1,000 feet (305m) difference in level between Allt Ddu and sea-level.

The partners tackled both routes, the overland route by the construction of new roads and the lake route by the building of an incline down the steep Allt Wen hillside. This system must have been expensive to work, and following the 1793 improvements at Moel y Don quay, later Felinheli, the use of Caernarfon was abandoned. In 1824 the overland Dinorwig Railway commenced operation and in 1842 the lake route was partially re-introduced by the opening of the Padarn Railway.

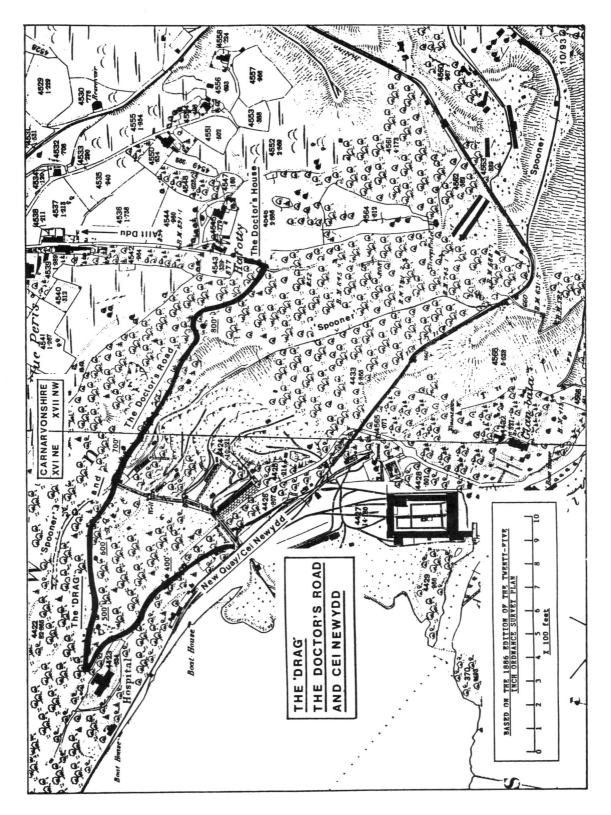

THE 'DRAG'
THE DOCTOR'S ROAD
AND CEI NEWYDD

BASED ON THE 1886 EDITION OF THE TWENTY-FIVE
INCH ORDNANCE SURVEY PLAN

X 100 feet

CARNARVONSHIRE
XVI NE   XVII NW

Looking down to the 'Drag'/Doctor's road hairpin

The Brynglas Tramways — looking north from SH 589605 1992

3. The First Railroad and Incline

On September 26th, 1788, one of the partners, William Bridge wrote to his colleague, Hugh Ellis, describing the transport difficulties which were hindering an increase in production.

"If 2,000 Countesses[9] per Day dragged down the Hill from Brynglas and from 1,500 to 2,000 also carr.d from thence on Horse back will supply the several orders at present for Slate, then you may depend upon being supplied with those Quantities I believe: but as to other sorts or greater Quantities to be sent from the Quarries at present, excepting Tun-Slate, is very uncertain. Every exertion is made and daily continued to be so, to do more, and it will be done if possible: but Dragging Slate down a steep Hill and carrying the Drag up again is so laborious and difficult a Task, that very few will undertake it at any price.

Eight Memel Dale Balk of 40 (12m) to 50 feet long (15.3m) and 13 (Inches (330mm) Square each, are immediately wanted, and I desire you will order them from Liverpool as soon as possible for Making of a Rail Road to convey the Slates down from Bryn Glas, to where the Carts can take them up; as we shall thereby with Rope and Windlas, 2 small Waggons and 3 labourers, be able to convey all the Slate down from those Quarries as fast as they can be raised and dressed by the Number of Hands now employed at those two Quarries. This appears to be the most eligible way to be put in Practice — both for Expedition and saving Expence. I have put my Engineer upon this Scheme. He has viewed the Premises, measured distances, etc and will be ready to prepare everything as soon as the Balk arrive at Caernarvon. And a good Rope well tarred be ordered to be sent with the Balk from Liverpool of ¾ths of an Inch (19mm) Diameter and 200 Fathoms (366m) in length.

£130 is the amount of Balance due to Workmen and if not paid soon, I must take Flight to avoid being murdered;- Getting Slates carried under your Castle (Caernarvon) will not save me."

Apart from the above letter, little is known about the "Rail Road" and incline, even the location is open to discussion. Lindsay[10] writes that the incline had been built by 1789, and that slates were being sent down to Cei Newydd on Llyn Padarn, prior to shipment to Penllyn and Cwm y Glo. However, Boyd[11]1 considers that the incline fell to Y Cei at the north-west end of Llyn Peris, and that it was the forerunner of the former

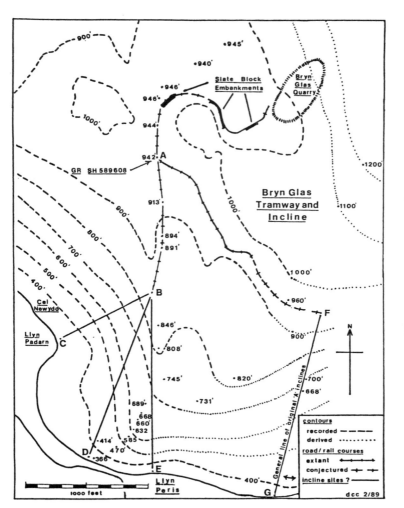

900'
•945'
•940'
Slate Block
Embankments
Bryn Glas Quarry
•946'
946'
944'
1000'
942' A
GR SH 589608
913'
1000'

Bryn Glas Tramway and Incline

1200'
1100'
•894'
•891'
800'
700'
600'
1000'
500'
B
400'
960'
F
Cei Newydd
900'
N
Llyn Padarn
C
•846'
•808'
•745'
•820'
700'
668'
D
689'
668'
660'
632'
585'
•414'
470'
•366'
E
•731'
General line of original 'A' inclines

Llyn Peris
400'
G

contours
recorded - - - - -
derived ·········
road/rail courses
extant ◄——►
conjectured +—+—+
incline sites ? ◄—►

1000 feet

dcc 2/89

Illus.3

*Was this the Bryn Glas tramway?
Embankment on minor road south of
Dinorwig bus turn-round
Site of Bryn Llys Quarry, left. 1992*

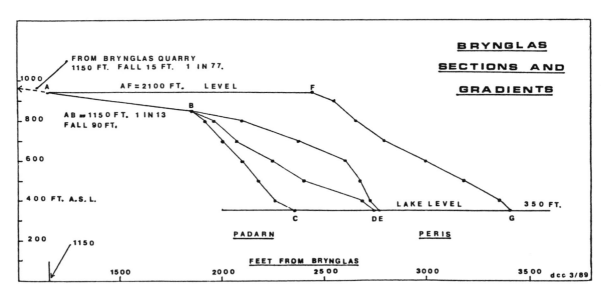

FROM BRYNGLAS QUARRY
1150 FT. FALL 15 FT. 1 IN 77.

1000

A
AF = 2100 FT. LEVEL
F

800

B
AB = 1150 FT. 1 IN 13
FALL 90 FT.

BRYNGLAS SECTIONS AND GRADIENTS

600

400 FT. A.S.L.

LAKE LEVEL
350 FT.

C
DE
G

PADARN
PERIS

200
1150

FEET FROM BRYNGLAS

1500
2000
2500
3000
3500

dcc 3/89

lower "A" inclines. Both routes were feasible, but a drop to the Peris side would have required ferrying the slate along the Afon y Bala, a waterway not noted for ease of navigation. Illsley[7] in a useful paper on the Llyn Padarn slate boats, includes a sketch-map showing an incline to Cei Newydd and a circuitous route, turning through 180 degrees, also terminating at Cei Newydd. Construction of this would have necessitated massive earth-works on the hillside. Despite the paucity of hard facts, it is interesting to speculate on the information available.

The problem was to lower the slate, some 600 feet (210m) (vertical equivalent), to the lake, 350 feet (107m) above sea-level. The Peris/Padarn hillside, as it is today, has a gradient of 1 in 2 (50%) to 1 in 3 (33.3%), say 1 in 2.5 or 25 degrees (40%). The shortest incline down such a hillside would require a rope 1,420 feet (433m) long, i.e. (600/sin25). As a first estimate, this agrees tolerably well with the 200 fathoms (1,200 feet) (360m) requested in the Bridge letter. Following subsequent quarrying, during the last 200 years, the physical features of the area have changed drastically, particularly on the Peris side. Some editions of the Ordnance Survey "six inch" map are contoured up to 1,000 feet (305m), but not in quarried areas. Fortunately, the contours on both sides of the excavations are approximately parallel and equidistant. With a little help from a number of bench marks and spot heights, along with some inter and extrapolation, a probable map can be prepared. Due allowance must be for the "deltas" created in the lakes by waste tipping.

For many years the local bus to Dinorwig village has turned round at the end of the public road. (591610) Throughout the life of the quarry, this site has been a centre of activity and communication. Brynglas and Chwarel Fawr quarries were in the near vicinity. A minor road still runs due south of the turn-round, and it is almost certain that it is the successor to the railroad built by the partners. It is not immediately obvious, but on the west side of the road, one can still see that the road is built on the top of a slate block embankment. Illus.3. It is fortunate that in the area there is an abundance of Ordnance Survey altitude data enabling an accurate section to be drawn.

At this point, it is necessary to consider the location of Brynglas quarry, long obliterated by thousands of tons of slate waste. The Ellis map shows Brynglas to be east of Allt Ddu quarry. Despite the limitations of the map, it is possible, by using the average Ellis map page size scale of 900 feet/inch, to obtain at least an indication of the site of Brynglas relative to a modern map. Until the "landscaping", there was visible evidence of old tramways in the vicinity of Brynglas. These were not casual or temporary structures, they were built on substantial vertical sided slate block embankments, twelve feet high, round the east and south sides of the south Allt Ddu or Adelaide quarry. These structures which are illustrated in Illus.4 were of comparitively early origin and a number of pierced slate block sleepers are still visible. Boyd has suggested that these works were part of an Adelaide avoiding line[12]. This could well be so, but could they have been of more significance? Perhaps they were the start of the 1788 Brynglas Tramway or a later development of it. The location was about right and consistent with a line to an incline top. When the district was "landscaped", the space either side of the embankment was filled in till flush with the sleepers; they may still be seen.

Returning to the minor road running south from the bus turn-round, could this also have been part of a Brynglas Tramway? Probably yes, although today it is some five feet (1.5m) lower. Referring to the diagram, it will be seen that the tramway would have started at the south-west end of Brynglas and immediately pass on to the block embankments. After turning through nearly 180 degrees, where the steeper part might have been, it proceeded to the south, along the "hidden" section of the embankment. After about 400 yards it arrived at point "A" (589608). From this point, a lane branches off to the south-east; but more about this later. The road continues to the south, the gradient steepening to 1 in 13 (7.7%). Following another 300 yards (274m), one passes a large house on the east side. This is Hafodty; one time home of the quarry general manager and later the quarry surgeon. At the present time, the site, "B" on the map, is surrounded by trees, but in earlier times one would have looked down the barren Allt Wen hillside to the Llynnau Peris and Padarn. There is evidence, both on the map and on the ground, of a road, descending through the trees, to Llyn Padarn. The road which was about 950 yards (870m) long, had a hairpin and fell 520 feet (159m), an average gradient of 1 in 6 (16.7%). It is tempting to speculate that in earlier times, it was the "drag" route. In later times it was the road from Hafodty to the quarry office at Gilfach Ddu and it became known as the Doctor's Road. The hairpin is still there, adjacent to the Country Park Centre, formerly the Quarry hospital. Close by there is short downhill track to the site of Cei Newydd.

Returning to the top of the hill; point "B" has been taken as a notional incline summit. Three possible

*Slate Block embankments
in the Allt Ddu —
Brynglas District*

Illus.4

incline routes are shown on the diagram, "BC" to Cei Newydd, "BD" to Glan y Bala and "BE" to Y Cei on Peris-side. Returning to point "A" and the lane to the south-east, this is also an eligible route. After a level 650 yards (595m.), it disappears under a slate tip. (The first quarry hospital was situated here until it was engulfed by slate waste). In earlier times, the lane or possibly tramway could have terminated at the top of the hillside above Llyn Peris; point "F" on the diagram. An incline route "FG" is also shown. Data on the four inclines is given below.

INCLINE	BC	BD	BE	FG
Length Feet	1005	1636	1646	1720
Gradient	1 in 2.0	1 in 3.3.	1 in 3.3.	1 in 3.4
Max. Gradient	1 in 1.5	1 in 2.0	1 in 3.0	1 in 1.9

Because of the geographical features in the Allt Ddu and Peris-Padarn areas, it is self-evident that as much level or near level routage as reasonable should be used. Equally, once an incline has been deemed necessary, it should be as short and consequently as steep as practicable. Such an incline would, in general, be more cost-effective in construction, capacity and operation than a long, shallow one. As far as the four examples are concerned, they all meet the criteria.

The first "One Inch" Ordnance Survey map of the district has already been referred to. The Allt Ddu group of quarries is shown and the embankment tramway and north-south lane can be identified. In addition, the probable route of the 1798 "drag" can be seen. As far as the first incline is concerned, there is no indication of a direct drop to Cei Newydd, i.e. "BC", A well developed incline system can be seen, but unfortunately no detail is shown. Starting at about 1,200 feet (366m) level, it descended in a number of stages to Peris side. During the descent there is a distinct "drift" to the east, with a final drop to half way along the Llyn Peris, north-east shore, in the area latterly known as Wellington or Muriau (*walls*). On the diagram, the lower part of the incline would have approximated to incline "FG". As the quarry developed, the lower half of the incline was overtaken by the excavations and today, no remains are visible. This incline can be considered to be the first of a series of three incline systems, that became known as the "A" inclines. In 1860 a print of the quarry, as seen from the south-west shore of Llyn Peris was published[13]. The print shows a replacement series of four inclines descending in a straight line to the north-east corner of Llyn Peris. Incidentally, as the quarry developed, these inclines were pushed further north-west, resulting in a final series descending to Padarn-side.

Which of the four proposals was adopted? All one can do is to examine the "fors and againsts" and make a choice. Starting with incline "BC"; the length of both the tramway from the quarry to the incline top, and the incline itself, would have been the shortest. In addition, the length of the rope required is nearest to the length ordered by William Bridge. The use of incline "BC" would have partly eliminated the ferrying of slate along the Afon y Bala. A final drop to Cei Newydd, suggests that comparitively new facilities would have been available. Regarding the other three proposals, all would have been longer, and with case "FG", the length of the tramway would also have been greater. Apart from a longer rope, a longer incline would have had a lower capacity for an equal number of waggons. All three would have needed sailings along the Afon y Bala. It is not easy to think of reasons for the proposals. It could be argued that "FG" could have been incorporated in to the later "A" inclines, but it is doubtful if such forward planning occurred; indeed the necessity to build such a series of "A" inclines would suggest just the opposite. Concentration of all loading at one point could have cost less, but the congestion would have been greater. On examining the 1889 "25 inch" Ordnance Survey plan there is a curious excavation in the vicinity of "E". This was about 40 yards (37m) long and 20 yards (18m) wide. A branch tramline ran in to it. It is directly on the line of proposal "BE". It will be seen from the diagram that the bottom of the incline was steep and could not be seen from the top. If this incline had been adopted, could the excavation have been to remove the "bump" and allow visual communication between top and bottom?

Whichever incline was chosen, the fact remains that for a first incline, 1,000 feet (305m) was a long one. By comparison, the longest inclines of later times were at the Port, 1,360 feet (415m) long and "C4" at the quarry, 1,000 feet (305m) long. Boyd[11] has proposed that it could have been shorter, starting lower down the hillside. It would have been possible to build a series of inclines; the total length of rope needed would not have been significantly greater. i.e. (Total number of inclines − 1) x circumference of the drum. However, a number of horizontal "landings" would have been necessary, but no such remains are evident. The William Bridge letter states that the scheme would be operated by three labourers. Any multi-stage system would surely have needed more than three men to work it. Still with the letter, it seems rather odd that only two waggons were to be ordered. It might have been that the two waggons were special ballast ones, permanently attached to each end of the rope. Regarding additional waggons and rails, it is not unreasonable to suggest that the tramway section was already in use, and the waggons and rails already available. At the time of the letter, self-acting inclines, on which the descending loaded waggons on one track haul up empty waggons on the adjacent track, were already well established. There is no reason why the incline was not of this type. The reasonable agreement between the estimated and ordered length of rope, indicates that there was only one wheel or drum, unlike later systems using two ropes and two drums on the same axle.

Some consideration must now be given to the eight timber balks listed in the letter. By any standard, these were large pieces of wood, the weight of each being about one ton. The name of the wood, Memel, suggests that they came from the Baltic; presumably this size was not available in Britain. One can imagine them being drawn up the hill from Caernarfon to Cwm y Glo and then floated along the lake. What were they for? A first thought might be that they were for incline sleepers. If so, there was only sufficient balk for ninety feet of twin track incline. Timber of these dimensions and source would have been expensive; who would have thought of cutting them up to make shorter lengths? Sleepers would have been either slate or timber from local sources. The incline was built and put to use very quickly, Lindsay writes[14] that it was ready by

1789, a mere three months, perhaps it might be more accurate to say during 1790. As construction was so rapid, could the balk have been to span a hollow or gulley, instead of building an embankment? Time would have been saved. It must not be forgotten that although Cei Newydd was already in use; it was on a smaller scale than required for the imminent increase in tonnage. A much larger quay or jetty had become necessary for the boats and carts mentioned in the letter. Of course, none of this now visible; it is under the Gilfach Ddu delta. When the size of the incline and the weight of slate are considered, it is evident that the winding drum or wheel would have to be supported and housed by a stout structure. Could at least some of the balk have been used for a drumhouse? Indeed, the Oxford Dictionary defines "balk" as a tie-beam of a house.

Returning to Boyd's proposal[11], that in practice the incline was somewhat less in length than when first considered. It would have been feasible to have had a somewhat shorter incline. Reference to the diagram will show that the top segment of incline "BC" could have been eliminated without causing serious difficulty. Returning to the question, which incline was built? The author has posed a number of questions which will probably never be answered. However, in the author's opinion, the best case can be made for incline "BC". If the transport of slate along the Afon y Bala had not been involved, incline "BE" would have been a serious contender.

Boyd[15] rightly debunks the claim that the Llandegai Tramway near Bangor was the first railway in North Wales, and suggests that it could only claim to be the first overland system in the district. Can the same claim be made for the Brynglas Tramway, which preceded the Llandegai by at least nine years?

4. Where did the Dinorwig Railway Start?

Today, more than one and a half centuries after it was built, much of the route of the Dinorwig Railway may still be walked. However, at the quarry end, all traces disappeared a long time ago; either with the excavations or under the evergrowing waste tips or "domen". Consequently, little has been written about the "lost" part of the old railway.

Two historic maps have been mentioned, the 1836 Lloyd Ellis map[1] and the 1841 1st. Edition "One Inch" Ordnance Survey Map. In the 1986 Boyd book, dealing with Dinorwig Quarry Railways there is a speculative map[16] showing a route at the quarry end of the railway; however, such a route would have incurred very severe gradients.

After all this time, is it feasible to write anything about the lost part? On resorting to a bit of "crystal gazing", it seems that something can be deduced about the nature of the "lost" railway. Reference has already been made to the anonymous, but relatively recent diagram of Dinorwig[3]. A number of the quarry locations on the diagram are also shown on the Ellis map; particularly Harriet, Morgans and Matilda. Collectively, these three sites formed part of the Dyffryn level; in latter-day nomenclature "C4".

Dyffryn is situated along the 1,000 foot contour. It can therefore be stated, with some confidence, that in the vicinity of the three quarries, the Dinorwig Railway was at this height. Before the 1980's "landscaping", a horizontal gallery from the Allt Ddu pits to the highest point (A, 969') of the road to the port could be clearly seen. It is very likely that at one time, it was on the line of the Dinorwig Railway.

The 1st. Edition Ordnance Survey map shows the route of the Dinorwig Railway but, as written by Harley, it could have been up to twenty years out of date. It seems, that in such an unreliable situation, the use of the map must be treated with some reserve. In the section on Maps and Plans, there is mention of the preparation of a "Six Inch" transparent enlargement of the "One inch" First Edition. If this is superimposed on a current "Six Inch" version, it can be seen that although the start point would have been at point "A", the general line has rotated clockwise through about twenty degrees. After ascending 141 feet (43m) over a distance of 2,568 feet (783m), the route would have crossed the later "A" inclines at a height of 1,100 feet (336m) above sea level. (D) The average gradient would have been 1 in 18 (5.6%), including a probable maximum gradient of 1 in 6.5 (15.4%) for the 648 feet (198m) long, final approach to A5T. (D) From this point, the overlay shows the track falling 100 feet (31m) along 1,546 feet (472m) to the 1,000 feet (305m) high Dyffryn level. (E) The mean gradient would have been 1 in 15 (6.7%), with a probable maximum gradient of 1 in 5.2 (19.2%) for 524 feet (160m). The O.S. map shows the line continuing in a near southerly direction with an indicated maximum gradient of 1 in 2.0 (50.0%). (F) This must surely be treated with scepticism. At such a location, the construction of worthwhile gradient reducing bends would have required massive constructions on the steep mountain-side. The thought of loads being hauled up a 1 in 5 (20.0%) grade, from the 1,000 feet high Dyffryn quarries, to a level of 1,100 feet, only to be returned to a near 1,000 feet, is not realistic. The map could be construed as showing an end to end junction between the railway and incline. This would have entailed a series of sloping "galleries". The idea is most unlikely, particularly when a near level, 1,000 foot contour railway could have been constructed with relative ease. The Ellis map confirms the premise. A plan showing heights, distances and gradients is appended. The near level route would have been serpentine in style, with a shallow cutting, about 200 feet (61m) long, across the neck of the granite bluff. (G) Today, there are parts where one might expect to find remains, but the author has found no convincing evidence. In addition, there are no indications on the 1888 "25 inch plan" or any of the aerial photographs. Bradley[17] has suggested that the previously mentioned block embankments at Brynglas-Alltddu formed part of the 1824 route. Illus.4. This would have necessitated a steep slope round the bluff, followed by an up grade of 1 in 40 (2.5%) for something like 1,200 feet back to the highest point (A). If built, it would have been a forerunner of the first "Village Branch".

In the author's opinion, the Ellis map, despite its limitations, provides the most likely approximation to a 1,000 feet contour line. As for the route shown on the Ordnance Survey map, there must be serious doubt about its validity.

There remains the challenge for some brave person to find some remains under the gorse and brambles that cover the granite bluff.

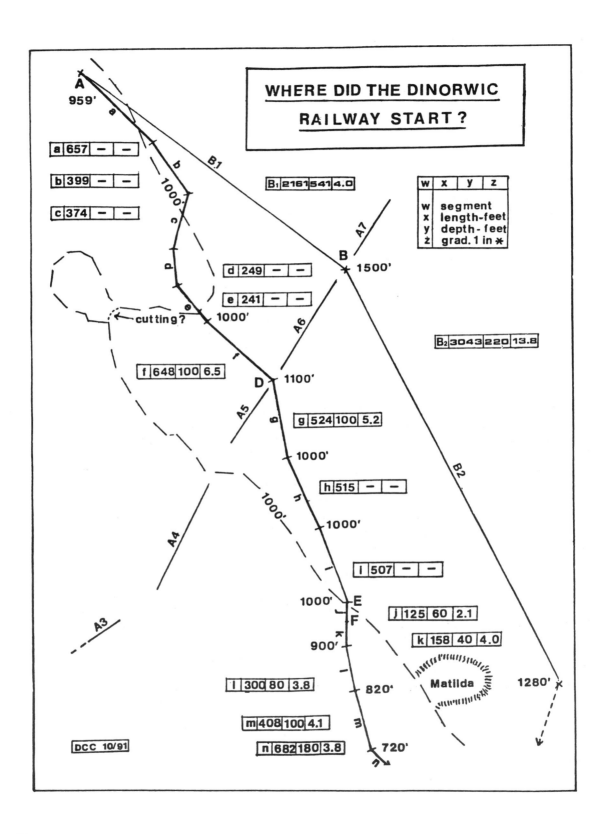

WHERE DID THE DINORWIC RAILWAY START ?

A
959'

a | 657 | — | —

b | 399 | — | —

c | 374 | — | —

B1

B₁ | 2161 | 541 | 4.0

A7

B
1500'

w	x	y	z
w	segment		
x	length-feet		
y	depth-feet		
z	grad. 1 in *		

d | 249 | — | —

e | 241 | — | —

A6

← cutting? 1000'

B₂ | 3043 | 220 | 13.8

f | 648 | 100 | 6.5

D 1100'

A5

g | 524 | 100 | 5.2

1000'

h | 515 | — | —

1000'

B2

A4

i | 507 | — | —

1000' E
F

j | 125 | 60 | 2.1

k | 158 | 40 | 4.0

900'

A3

l | 300 | 80 | 3.8

Matilda 1280'

820'

m | 408 | 100 | 4.1

720'

n | 682 | 180 | 3.8

DCC 10/91

5. The Spooner Survey
(An investigation of G.A.S. Vaynol 7142)

For many years little was known about the relics stored away in the Faenol House; the limited number available had come from quarry sources. They were not indexed and in most cases it was a matter of luck that they had survived. It is known that a number of documents were deliberately destroyed when the quarry ceased work. The Management did not appreciate their value and in any case, took the view that they were family matters, not the business of the public.

During the late 1960's the author was fortunate to be "tipped off" about the "Spooner Survey". Following an enquiry to the Faenol Estate, the author was advised by Sir Michael's secretary, that he was a few days too late; they had been transferred to the County Archivist for safekeeping. The work of cataloguing was undertaken by Mrs Mary Aris, who kindly let the author have an early sight of the Survey. However, this did cause some confusion, as it had received a temporary catalogue number, which the author quoted in the first edition of *Slates to Velinheli*.

The *Spooner Survey*, which is undated, was undertaken by Spooner and Sons, as a possible replacement of the 1824 Dinorwig Railway. It takes the form of a watercoloured strip map some 12 feet 4 inches long (3.76m.) and 2 feet four inches wide. (0.71m.) It is a curious document and initially, one wonders whether to treat it on a serious or casual basis. For example, the title on the map, "A proposed railway from Port Dinorwig to Dinorwig Slate Quarries" uses no less than seven different size and print styles. The quarry is labelled, DINORWIG SLATE QUARRIES. This is strange; Dinorwi*g*, ending with a "g" was unusual at the time, and in addition, the word has smaller letters than SLATE QUARRIES. There are two versions of the word "Dolbadarn". Llyn Padarn is called "Dolbad*e*rn Lake" but the castle is spelt in the usual way; with an "a". One's first thought could well be, was it another Porthmadog "doodle"[18].

When was it drawn? The map shows the 1824 Dinorwig Railway as "existing railway". It does not show the 1842 Padarn Railway. Therefore as a first estimate, it can be stated that it was drawn in the period 1824-1842. Can a more precise date be deduced? Yes, the map shows that the proposed route passed through Shelton and Greaves quarry (577615), which was situated on the Fachwen hillside above Llyn Padarn. The quarry was worked on land leased by Lord Newborough to Edwin Shelton, who in 1840, complained to his lordship that Spooner was surveying a railway across the land leased from his lordship[19]. We now have a precise date for the Survey. Bearing in mind the manner in which the quarry was to develop, was a survey of a railway, some 200 feet (61.0m) above lake level, a serious proposition?

A scale of 10 inches = 3,000 feet is included with the Survey; which can be re-stated as one inch = 100 yards. There are a couple of minor clerical errors with the scale labelling. Along the line of the route, there are a series of letters, "A" to "K". These are not equidistant and "F" and "J" are not shown. There is a note stating that the letters refer to a "section" of the railway. As far as the author is aware, this has not survived. There is no shortage of "landmarks" that can be located on modern maps of proven accuracy. The distances between fourteen of these has been calculated using the Ordnance Survey 25 inch and 6 inch maps as standards. The Spooner scale has also been calculated for each increment and these are shown in the table below.

Location	Map Ref SH	Spooner inches	OS length inches	OS Scale 6/25	Ord.Sur yards	Spooner scale
GlanyBala	587 602	-	-	-	-	-
		7.1	10.0	25	704	99
Hairpin	583 607	-	-	-	-	-
		8.0	11.4	25	803	100
Afon Fach	578 612	-	-	-	-	-
		4.3	6.2	25	436	102
Shelton Q	577 615	-	-	-	-	-
		12.3	17.8	25	1253	102
Llech y F	566 619	-	-	-	-	-
		4.3	6.5	25	458	106

Bron Gadw	568 622	-	-	-	-	-
		8.0	11.5	25	810	101
Bryn Teg	571 629	-	-	-	-	-
		12.2	4.6	6	1349	108
Cae Bled	561 637	-	-	-	-	-
		15.0	5.2	6	1536	102
Gorse	559 651	-	-	-	-	-
		20.2	6.9	6	2024	100
Groeslon	559 669	-	-	-	-	-
		11.8	4.1	6	1203	102
Pont Wylf	551 676	-	-	-	-	-
		5.7	8.3	25	384	103
TynyCoed	546 678	-	-	-	-	-
		7.1	10.4	25	732	103
TanyWylfa	543 673	-	-	-	-	-
		9.8	3.6	6	1056	107
Penscoins	535 678	-	-	-	-	-

The mean of the Spooner scales is 102.7, with a range of 99 to 108. On the face of it this appears to be rather wide, but it cannot be interpreted as a criticism of the accuracy and precision of Spooner. The locations are not spot sites, some being as wide as a quarter of an inch, or some 25 yards (22.8m) on the ground. It would be possible to have an unknown error of 50 yards (45.6m) on any one increment. For those interested in statistics the Standard Deviation is $+/-2.7$. The author is in no doubt that, as drawn, the survey was done to a high standard. It was certainly not a Porthmadog "doodle", but a serious investigation in to finding a replacement for the Dinorwig Railway.

Commencing at the quarry end, where did the proposed railway commence? The survey shows the start to be at "K", 700 yards (641m) north-east of Dolbadarn Castle. (586588) If this vector is transferred to a modern map, the start point would be at (592602), 668 feet (204m) above sea-level. This point is of some significance, in that it is on a gallery named Victoria; it may still be visited. Queen Victoria came to the throne in 1837, a time when a new railway would have been under consideration. Unfortunately, there is no location on the survey enabling, anything like, a right-angle "cross fix" to be obtained. There is a strong hint of an incline, 200 yards (183m) long, in a southerly direction, possibly one of the original "A" inclines. Such an incline, which would have had a gradient of 1 in 2.6 (38%), terminated on Peris-side. Following the digression, a description of the present day (1993 Victoria level may be useful. Beginning at "K"; after a few yards walk, we pass, on the right hand side, a large compressor house, dated 1938. On peeping inside, the two compressors, still in moderate condition, are still there. They were too big for the scrap dealer to take away. Continuing along the line there is visible evidence of early sleepers, both the pierced slate and cast iron types. After some 500 yards (458m), the latterday "A" incline system is reached. The survey shows that the tramway would have entered a tunnel, 210 yards (192m) long, through an impeding rock bluff. However, a tunnel was not built; its place being taken by a shelf round the bluff. At this point, the route is blocked by the later "A4" incline drum house. The path can be easily recognised on the far side. It has become a very attractive walk along a now well wooded hillside. The trackbed is built on a random stone block structure, and the point where a tunnel would have emerged, can be recognised. After a further 300 yards (280m) the route is again impeded; this time by the later Vivian quarry.

The works continue on the other side of the excavation. It can be regained by way of the already mentioned Doctor's Road hairpin (583607). At the top, the survey route is rejoined. If one goes to the right the now derelict but attractive "V4" incline drumhouse is soon passed on the right; and after a short distance the northwest side of the impeding quarry is reached. Returning to the Doctor's Road; the survey route continues northwest along the block embankment for a further 250 yards (229m), before coming to a sudden end. After a level 1,500 yards (1,281m) from "K", the path has run out. There are no obvious physical reasons as to why?

When Spooner produced his drawing to a scale of 100 yards = one inch, he was not to know, what a good turn he had done for the late 20th. Century researcher. The scale can be restated as 17.6 inches = one mile.

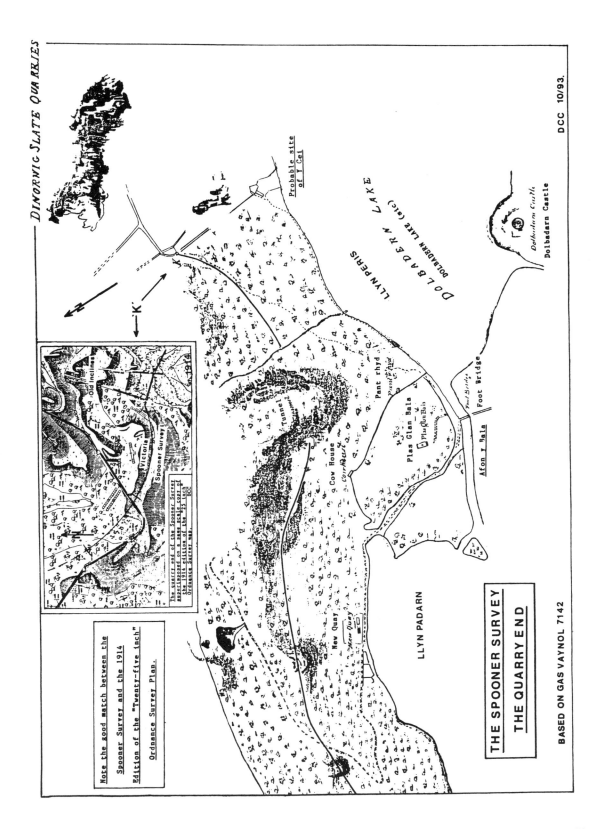

DINORWIC SLATE QUARRIES

Probable site of Y Cei

DOLBADARN LAKE (sic)

LLYN PERIS

DOLBADARN LAKE

Dolbadarn Castle
Dolbadarn Castle

Pant rhyd

Tunnel

Cow House

Plas Glan Bala

Plas Glan Bala

Afon y Bala

Foot Bridge

LLYN PADARN

New Quay
New Quay

Old Inclines

Victoria

Spooner Survey

The quarri end of the Spooner Survey
superimposed on a same scale copy of
the 1914 edition of the "25 inch"
Ordnance Survey map.   DCC

Note the good match between the
Spooner Survey and the 1914
Edition of the "Twenty-five inch"
Ordnance Survey Plan.

THE SPOONER SURVEY

THE QUARRY END

BASED ON GAS VAYNOL 7142

DCC 10/93.

25

Spooner Survey
Point K.
Outside 1938 Compressor
House. 1993
Looking west

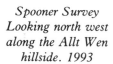

Spooner Survey
Looking north west
along the Allt Wen
hillside. 1993

Spooner Survey
Looking north west
from impeding A4
drumhouse. 1993

A4 incline down
to left, rail
still in situ

The modern "DIN" system of paper sizes is based on an up factor of 1.4 and a down factor of $1/1.4 = 0.7$. e.g. An A4 sheet can be enlarged to A3 by adjusting the copier factor to 1.4. The enlarged copy has a scale of 25 inches = 1 mile, the same as the Ordnance Survey large scale plan. Using this technique it is a simple matter to compare the Spooner survey directly with modern plans. On transferring the data from Spooner to a reduced scale O.S. "25 inch" plan, it will be seen that in the vicinity of "K", there is a good match in scale, "shape" and especially the two incline sites shown on both maps.

The contours of the Allt Wen hillside are evenly spaced, enabling simple gradient calculations to be made. Initially, the survey route is more or less parallel with the contours but west of the termination of the embankment, it starts to veer to the west, and lose height. After crossing the 600 foot contour the track would have levelled off at about 520 feet (159m), a drop of 148 feet (39m). It is impossible to be precise about the length of the downhill part of the route, but the author estimates it to be about nine inches on the "25 inch" plan. This equates to 1,902 feet (585m) on the ground. The downhill section would have had a gradient in the order of 1 in 13 (7.7%), i.e. 1,902/(668-520). Such a steep grade is surprising for a line planned as late as 1840, particularly if locomotives were envisaged. On the other hand, the heavy loaded trains would be going downhill and the empties going uphill. Before turning north, round a 35 yard (32m) radius bend, the line came to within 85 yards (78m) of the lake side. From this point, the proposed route moved between the 500 feet and 600 feet contours for 300 yards, suggesting that some embankment work would have been required.

In 140 yards (128m), the line commenced another long curve, this time anti-clockwise, turning through 110 degrees with a mean radius of 280 yards. (256m) About half way round the bend, the Afon Fachwen would have been crossed on a Dolgoch type viaduct. Today, at a somewhat lower level, there are remains of an estate road bridge over the stream. At the end of the bend there are still the remains of Shelton and Greave's quarry, the site of Spooner's illicit surveying. In a short distance, the estate road regains its lost height; there is no doubt that it is exactly on the Spooner route. It is a beautiful situation with good views over the Llyn Padarn. Still at an altitude of 500 feet (153m), the route runs nearly parallel to the lakeside for a further 650 yards (595m). From this point there is a change of view, the route gradually turns away from the lakeside to a different type of scene. After passing through two tunnels, under the Coed y Clegyr (569621), 80 yards (73m) and 240 yards (220m) long, the track would have emerged in to a totally different type of scenery. Here was a wilder landscape, a hillside littered with numerous rocky outcrops. In order to maintain a level of 500 feet (153m), it would have been necessary to build an embankment followed by a shelf cut, or blasted out of a near vertical rock face. The line would have continued its way, in an east by north direction, across the sinuous 500 feet (153m) contour, by means of a series of embankments and complementary excavations. The route of the survey can be followed, there being a number of readily recognised buildings, some now derelict, on both the survey and map. In one place, the survey route would have coincided with a footpath shown on the map. After 650 yards (595m), the survey approaches a step or fault across the valley. This necessitated another big bend turning through 100 degreees along an anti-clockwise 150 yard (137m) radius curve. Much of the bend would have been on an embankment and bridge over the Afon Caledffrwd. About 100 yards (91.5m) upstream, the river still tumbles over the "step" forming quite a respectable waterfall. After about 440 yards in a southwest direction and at a height of 500 feet (153m), the route started a gradual turn to the north. At the same time it descended to 450 feet (137m), over 250 yards (229m), a sudden gradient of 1 in 15 (6.7%). The survey does not show any civil engineering works but a gradient easing cutting and embankment would seem to have been essential. For the next 800 yards (732m) the route went due north, during which it dropped in to the shallow valley of the Afon Waen Fidel; Afon Cegin on later maps, 400 feet (122m) above sea level. A gradient of about 1 in 30 would have been involved.

On the way north, point "G" (561646) is passed, where the track would have crossed a stream. Similarly, point "E" (561663) was also at a bridge site over a stream. The whole area is more or less flat, probably with serious drainage problems. About 350 yards (320m) past "E", the survey route crossed the 1824 route. "Stabla Newydd" (660664) was on the west side and after a further 500 yards (458m), the 1824 route was again crossed at Croeslon, 365 feet (111m) above sea level. Following a bend to the west there would have been a fall, 300 yards (274m) long with a gradient of 1 in 45 (2.2%), to Pant y Wylfa. The survey shows the line entering a well wooded section within which, it parts company with the 1824 line, which carried straight on to the Garth incline. The Spooner proposal turned anti-clockwise round a ninety degree curve of 200 yards (183m) radius. Tyn y Coed would have been passed on the north side. The gradient would have been a gradual 1 in 150 (0.67%). In a further 400 yards (366m) at "D" (542675), yet another big curve would have begun, this time turning through ninety degrees to the west with a radius of 500 yards (458m). A final straight stretch of 450 yards (412m) followed by a 45 degree curve of 220 yards (201m) radius would have terminated at the top of an incline "C" (532679) down to Port Dinorwig quay ("B" and "A"). According to the survey, it would have been 300 yards (275m) long with a gradient of 1 in 3 (33.3%) Today, if one stands across the road from the *Half Way House* hotel at Port Dinorwig (529670) and looks inland, the severity of the incline can be visualised. Some 120 yards (110m) to the south, the 1842 Port incline was constructed on a longer parallel line.

There is no doubt that the survey was an accurate piece of work, matching well the shape and size of surviving features at the quarry end. With a few gradient easing devices, it would have been suitable for the steam locomotive. One of the big disadvantages of the 1824 Dinorwig Railway was that it started at the 1,000 foot (305m) level; any slate produced below this level had to be lifted to the railhead. The Spooner proposal to start a replacement railway at a height of more than 300 feet (91.5m) above the lake is surprising; it would have perpetuated the main disadvantage of the Ellis route; slate would still have to have been lifted to the railhead. The survey shows that at heights lower than "G", there were trees and no indication of quarry working. On the other hand, there is at least one drawing showing that by 1850, quarrying activity down to lake level was well established[13].

The Padarn Railway, the final solution to the problem of conveying slate to Port Dinorwig, cost £35,000 to build in the early 1840's. At the time, such an amount was a vast sum of money. Such expense must have encouraged the proprietor to seriously reconsider the lower capital cost but higher running cost, of the less convenient, narrow gauge, Spooner route. If the railway had been built, it would have been seven and three quarter miles long. It must have been touch and go as to whether the Padarn Railway was ever built.

The upper half of the survey route is very scenic and well worth forsaking the car. Apart from the accessible parts already mentioned, there is easy access to Shelton and Greaves (Faenol) quarry from the narrow road (576628) from Penllyn to Dinorwig village. Easy access to another attractive part of the survey route may be obtained by a hilly south east track from near Bryn Refail school (628661). The Afon Caledfrwydd waterfall is very close to the old "slate road" (571631).

Looking across Llyn Padarn to Pen y Bigil. The Spooner Survey route
was along the hillside. The Padarn Railway embankment is on the far
side of the lake and the trackbed of the L.N.W.R.
Llanberis branch is in the foreground

6. The Chwarel Fawr — Allt Ddu Complex and Allied Topics

At this point, it becomes necessary to consider in more detail, some of the points mentioned in the introductory chapters. When slate first started to be used as a building material, it was no doubt, picked up where an outcrop broke the surface. The early methods of quarrying would have been simple, labour intensive, and unsuitable for large scale production. However, as demand increased, the local quarriers began to organise themselves in to a more cohesive venture; so much so, that by 1787, it was no longer a "cottage industry". However, if the industry was to expand, new large scale techniques had become necessary. As far as Dinorwig is concerned, these were initially provided by the three partners who had acquired the concession from Assheton Smith. The digging would have been either horizontal in to a hillside, producing a visible "scar" or vertically, resulting in a "sinc" or pit. Whichever method was adopted, the main priority would have been to achieve the highest tonnage for the lowest cost; little consideration would have been given as to how future working was to develop. For example, the Dinorwig "Great New Quarry" was seriously inconvenienced due to a lack of forward planning in the early days, in that a series of retreating "C" inclines had to be built as the quarry advanced. Nevertheless, the site selected for Chwarel Fawr, 1,000 feet above sea level and adjacent to the slopes of the valley of the Afon Fachwen (*little white stream*) was an inspired choice, but as explained later the location was never fully exploited. Following the initial excavations, a pit going ever deeper was dug and as development proceeded, it would have been relatively easy to bore a serious of horizontal tunnels or adits, from the current pit bottom, to the open hillside. The tunnels provided a relatively easy means of removing slate and waste to the outside slopes, but equally improtant, they provided a ready means of draining the pit. By comparison, the big pit quarries in the Nantlle district, required all slate and rubbish to be removed vertically by lifting, and drainage water by pumping. (The Dorothea pit (499532) was more than 500 feet (155m) deep.) In commercial terms, this must have been very much to the advantage of Dinorwig. It is remarkable that although Chwarel Fawr, Brynglas and Allt Ddu, all "sinc"s, were initially independent of one another, they came to share the same complex incline systems.

Until the 1980's "landscaping" of the Allt Ddu district, there were the remains of much of the early works. Alas, it is now covered by an unimaginatvie grassed over area. The author often regrets that he did not visit the area more often. To a large extent, the student of today has to fall back on maps and the not too common surface and aerial photographs. It is now more difficult to determine altitudes of quarry sites; but if two reasonable assumptions are made, realistic estimations are possible. The first assumption is that local connecting tramway was level and the second, that inclines had a constant gradient. If the altitude at the top and bottom is known, intermediate altitudes can be readily calculated by using the incline as a scaling tool; although it must not be overlooked that inclines have been built on embankments. e.g. the Dinorwig "C" series is a good example, although in this case the heights are well recorded.

The 1836, R. Lloyd Ellis map has already been described in the section on maps and plans, but it warrants further consideration. Although lacking in detail, it shows that the quarry had become a sizeable industrial site. It does not show a great deal of railway detail and it seems that it was drawn largely for land area and geological reasons. However, it does show part of the 1824 tramway to the port. The tramway is labelled "Dinorwic Railway"; the only contemporary reference, known to the author, giving the tramway a name. Apart from a loop system at the top of an incline, there is no indication of additional trackwork. The original of the map is not too clear, but a tracing has been prepared and reduced to quarto. Illus.1. Can the map be compared with later surveys? Because of a shortage of "anchor points", it is not easy to make a comparison. However, the author has located four points which can be related, with some confidence, to later maps having a reliable scale. It has been shown earlier that by using these points, an idea of the scale of the map can be calculated. The north/south scale is significantly different to the east/west one, and as the latter has been derived from only one measurement, it must be treated with some care. The location of a "Sawing Mill", at the **bottom** of the incline, suggests that there was already a tunnel from the then bottom of Chwarel Fawr. Later plans indicate that the top and bottom of the incline, (A and B) were 954 feet (291m) and 895 feet (273m) above sea level respectively. Using the original Ellis (A4) map scale of 536 feet/inch, the incline can be calculated to have been (536 X 0.95") = 509 feet (155m) long, with a gradient of 1 in 509/(953-895), i.e. 1 in 8.8. (11.4%). On the 25" plan, 509 feet (155m) equates to 2.4 inches (61mm), and on transferring this to the 25" Plan, the author was gratified to find an excellent agreement with Ellis. (Perhaps a bit of luck was

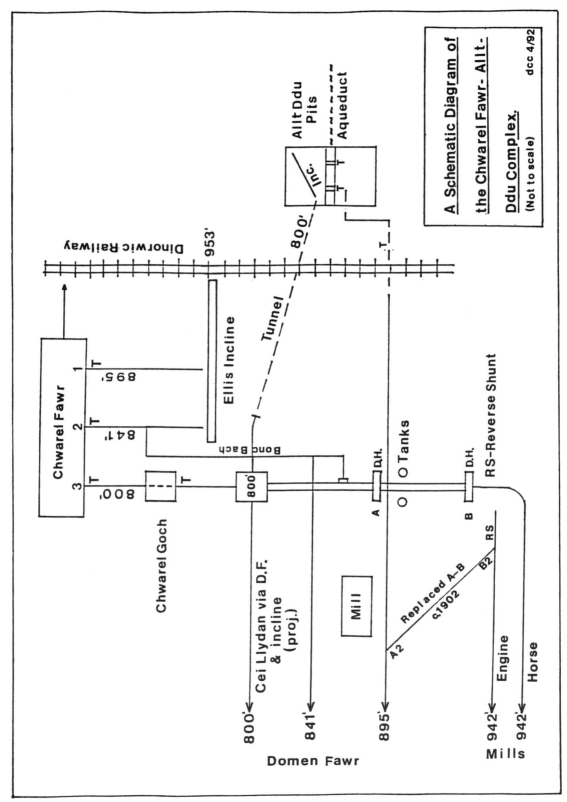

A Schematic Diagram of
the Chwarel Fawr- Allt-
Ddu Complex.
(Not to scale)   dcc 4/92

30

The Bonc Fawr tramway and embankment. The tramway from the bottom of the incline to Chwarel can be seen on the left under the bushes

The Bonc Fawr connection to the Chwarel Fawr incline. c.1980

The big Bonc Fawr embankment. The connection to Allt Ddu went through the tunnel at the base

also involved.) The top would have been at a level of 954 feet (291m) and the bottom, a 895 feet (273m); a height where, at a later date, an incline top and drum house was built; this was to become the all important Chwarel Fawr incline.

The 1st. Edition of the "25 inch" O.S. Plan of 1889 shows a tramway bridging the Chwarel Fawr incline at the 840 foot (256m) level. This was the Bonc Bach, (*little gallery*), which connected the Chwarel Fawr pit with the Domen Fawr (*big tip*). At one point the line was carried on a 40 feet (12m) high slate-block embankment over the Afon Fachwen and the 800 feet line from Allt Ddu. Access to Chwarel Fawr was by a tunnel, 258 feet (79m) long; and it entered the pit 121 feet (37m) below the surface. It is probable that this was not the first tunnel in to the pit, as on later maps there is a suspicion of earlier access at the 932 feet (284m) level. The tunnel would have been something like 100 feet (31m) long, entering the pit, about 25 feet (7.6m) below the surface. There is no indication of tunnel access above this level, but on some plans, there is a hint of an incline to the Dinorwig Railway. One must therefore assume that until the pit was 25 feet (7.6m) deep, all rock had to be lifted out by hoist; but more about Chwarel Fawr later.

The first "One Inch" Ordnance Survey Map of the district, which was published in 1841, has already been mentioned. Apart from the Dinorwig Railway, which is clearly shown, there are few of the features shown on the Ellis map. The Allt Ddu and Bryn Glas pits can be identified, the former being linked by a tramway, under the Dinorwig Railway, to a 700 feet (214m) long incline, presumably having a similar function to the later Chwarel Fawr one. A separate tramway is also shown starting from Brynglas, on the line of that proposed in an earlier chapter. The location of Chwarel Fawr can be recognised by the kink in the Dinorwig Railway.

Roundabout the time the "One Inch" map was being surveyed, the Dinorwig Railway must have been close to full capacity. If the tonnage of slate produced was to be increased, a new railway had become essential. Construction of the lakeside Padarn Railway commenced in 1841 and it was in service by March 1843. Consequent on this strategic change was the necessity to re-route all the Chwarel Fawr and Allt Ddu output. No doubt, further consideration would have given to a direct route down the Afon Fachwen valley, to join the new four foot gauge line at a lakeside interchange.

Such a valley line or incline would have been relatively simple to build. It could have taken the form of a single incline, some 3,500 feet (1068m) long, with a gradient of 1 in 7 (14.2%). However in theory, such a system would not have been as efficient as a 1,900 feet (580m) long tramway along the Domen Fawr 800 feet contour, terminating above the lake. A final drop to the lakeside at Cei Llydan, would have been by a 1,500 feet (458m) long incline, which would have included a 500 feet (153m) long section having a gradient of 1 in 2 (50%); the idea was not pursued. A similar 800 foot waste line was actually built to the end of the Domen Fawr; an incline from the end of this would have included a section with a gradient of 1 in 0.75, (133%); it was not built. At a later date the idea of an incline from the Domen Fawr to Cei Llydan was re-introduced, but this was for a different reason and will be discussed later.

In 1887, the Ordnance Survey surveyed the first "Twenty Five Inch" plans of the area. Only a glance is necessary to appreciate the big changes that had taken place since the publication of the "One Inch" map. Immediately obvious is an incline built on the hillside. This is the Chwarel Fawr incline, already referred to. It must have had a varied usage as there are design and operational differences in the three relevant map editions. One has to be careful not to infer too much from the maps and plans, but there are certainly some intriguing possibilities to be investigated.

On the mountain side behind Allt Ddu, the 1886 plan shows the Afon Fachwen labelled "aqueduct", but more about this later. Measurements from the map suggest that the incline was 832 feet (254m) long with a gradient 1 in 6.0 (16.7%). An indication of how the undertaking had grown is the tramway that ran from the Allt Ddu pit, 800 (244m) foot level, to the west end of the Domen Fawr, a distance of 3,000 feet (915m), over half a mile (805m), of which 750 feet (229m) were in tunnel. At the bottom of the incline there was a sharp bend to the west and a junction with the tramway just mentioned. The top of the incline had an end to end junction with the uphill tramway to "Steam Mills". (This tramway is dealt with in a separate chapter.) About a third of the way down the incline, at the 895 foot (273m) level, there was a turn-out to a slate mill and a tip line to Domen Fawr. In addition, at this level, there was a connection to a gallery near the top of the Allt Ddu pit.

The plan shows the Bonc Bach line from Chwarel Fawr passing over the incline on its way to the Domen Fawr but there is no connection with the incline. There is a hint, in the form of a levelled area, that one might have been under construction. The plan clearly shows that at the bottom of the incline, a cutting had been dug on the bearing of an unfinished track and tunnel to the bottom of Chwarel Fawr. It is surprising that a branch off the Bonc Bach line, to near the bottom of the Ellis incline, is still shown. If the plan is to be believed, there was no way of removing slate from the bottom of Chwarel Fawr. This illustrates the danger of inferring too much from a map, which represents what the surveyor recorded on perhaps, just one visit. The bottom of the incline must have been a very congested place, particularly as the stables for the horses were also sited there. Some smart traffic control must have been necessary to regulate the horses and waggons in the single track Allt Ddu tunnel.

A puzzling feature of the first edition plan is that although the incline was built on an embankment, calculated to be 20-25 feet (7.0m) wide, it only carried a single track along the full length. Assuming the plan is correct, the provision of a single track is surprising; a balanced incline would have simplified operation and increased capacity. However, it is possible that the incline was worked in a somewhat unusual manner. If we look at the position of the mill relative to the incline, it will be seen that the lower part was associated with raw slate going up and waste going down. The upper part dealt with processed slate going up; in other words, it could have been a balanced incline on a single track.

In 1899 the "1st. Revision" or "2nd. Edition" of the "Six Inch" and "Twenty five Inch" maps was surveyed; they were published in 1902. There do not appear to have been any major changes, although, as expected, there is now a turn out off the 841 foot Bonc Bach tip line to a side loading wharf on the incline. A completed route from the bottom of the incline to Chwarel Fawr still shows no rail, but after eleven years, it would seem to be more of an omission than fact.

In 1912/13 the "2nd. Revision" was surveyed. It was published in 1914. As far as the quarry was concerned, it was to be the last significant plan from the Ordnance Survey. The changes since the previous editions are immense; a completely new strategy had come in to use. The tunnel connection to the bottom of Chwarel Fawr is shown to have been completed. On the earlier plan, the Chwarel Goch (*red quarry*) was shown to be on the line of the tunnel. The new plan indicates that this small quarry had been incorporated in to the tunnel, the track now being visible from the surface. As the tunnel was 600 feet (183m) long, the hole might have been for ventilation purposes. (It must be borne in mind that the tunnel was only about four feet (1.2m) wide.) The function of the incline had completely changed, indeed the part above the mill level has been replaced by a deviation tramway. This is of such importance, as to warrant a separate section.

The now truncated incline was mainly twin track, but about 150 feet (48m) from the bottom, the two tracks merged to form a three track system, the centre rail being shared by both transporter's inner flangeless wheels. At the foot of the incline there was a side loading wharf for material arriving from the bottom of Chwarel Fawr. The Domen Fawr tip line, which also started from the bottom has been abandoned, along with the long tunnel connection with the Allt Ddu pit. The Bonc Bach wharf was still

The 800' route from the bottom of the Chwarel Fawr incline to the Domen Fawr, and projected routes to Cei Llydan and Gilfach Ddu. c.1980

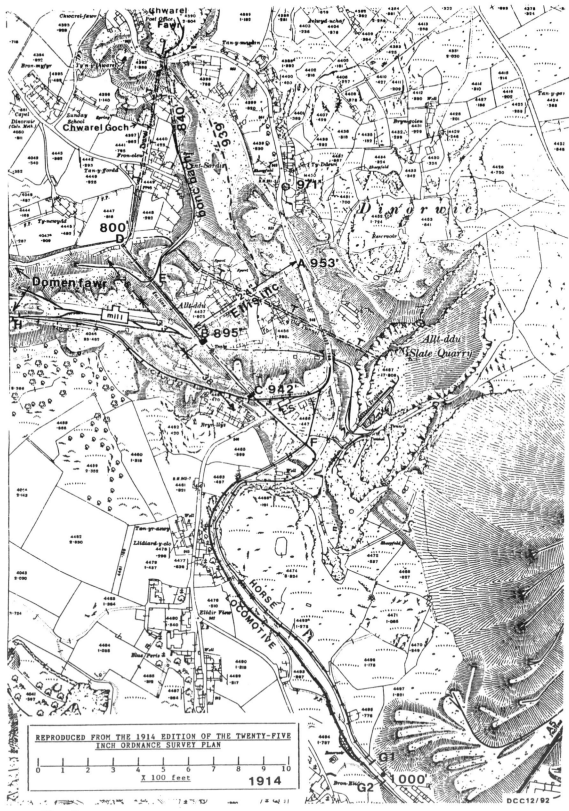

REPRODUCED FROM THE 1914 EDITION OF THE TWENTY-FIVE
INCH ORDNANCE SURVEY PLAN

0 1 2 3 4 5 6 7 8 9 10

X 100 feet

1914

DCC12/92

34   Illus.5

present, but only usable on the north-east track; i.e. the right side when looking down the incline. Illus.5. The summit of the new incline was also unusual, in that there were separate staggered wharves at the two transporter positions. The peculiar arrangements of the incline are strange, as there would seem to be so many impediments to simple working.

Let us consider the three rail arrangements at the bottom of the incline. Because of the shared third rail only the north-east side could be loaded. When the other transporter was at the bottom there would have been a gap between it and the wharf, unless a bridging piece could be fitted. There could well have been similar difficulty at the intermediate wharf, but no such difficulty at the top, where the plan shows that each track had a separate wharf. How was the incline powered? The author has considered whether the south-west track could have been a slate waste ballast track. This would seem to be unlikely as, in total, there would be a greater weight of raw slate to go up than the weight of rubbish going down. In addition there would have been the necessity to dispose of the rubbish at the bottom. Could it have been a water-balance incline? The Afon Fachwen aqueduct, behind Allt Ddu has already been mentioned. The word "aqueduct" suggests a purpose built or modified water-way. Allt Ddu quarry was actually two adjacent pits separated by a thin rock wall, which had been pierced at a number of levels for communication purposes. The wall could not be removed as it carried the aqueduct. There is further evidence on the plan; the word "tanks" is printed across the track site at the bottom of the abandoned upper part of the incline; 876 foot (267m) above sea-level. There would have been no difficulty disposing of the water at the bottom, the Afon Fachwen was already there. As for the original upper section, the plan shows that, apart from Bryn Goleu, a very small domestic supply reservoir on the top of the previously mentioned granite bluff, there was no water supply available high enough to ballast an incline. One wonders how the little reservoir was filled? As electricity had not arrived in the district, the alternative was the construction of a locomotive worked deviation tramway. Returning to the first incline, how was it powered in the absence of water? The alternatives are horse power, waste ballast and a steam engine. The Rev. Herbert Thomas who, as a child, lived in the vicinity, remembers a derelict structure at the incline summit, presumably a drum house. This supported a large horizontal cog-wheel, some confirmation that the incline was mechanically powered. The adjacent Allt Ddu pit incline was worked by a steam engine. There is no reason why the Chwarel Fawr incline was not originally powered in the same manner.

The final 1912 plan shows a new slate mill adjacent to the truncated incline summit. It is recorded that this was built in 1906[20]. The mill was a milestone in the district, in that, it and the mill at Steam Mills were equipped for electrical operation. In addition, the incline was converted to electric working and it is said that each track could be worked independently of the other, surely an indication of difficulty at the wharfs. The power was generated at the pioneer hydro-electric power station at Cwm Dyli in Nant Gwynant[21]. Electricity was also supplied to the Oakley quarry at Blaenau Ffestiniog.

Note
The calculations employed in connection with the Chwarel Fawr, Allt Ddu and Village Branch chapters, are included as an Appendix.

The Chwarel Fawr incline drumhouse. Note the low level drum due to the side loading incline. 1980

Photograph from Lon Garret (Garret Road)
Grid Reference SH 574 603. 1,275 feet above
sea-level

A.	nil.
B4	Llanberis
B5	Llanberis
B6	Llanberis
C13	Domen Fawr, levelled area
C14	Domen Fawr, levelled area
C15	Domen Fawr
C16	Domen Fawr, Llyn Padarn
C17	Llyn Padarn
D15	Domen Fawr
D16	Domen Fawr
D17	Domen Fawr
E15	Start of deviation tramway to Allt Ddu
F1	Locomotive worked "village branch"
F4	Paved road, possibly Bryn Glas tramway to inclince top
F6	Bryn Llys quarry
F7	Bryn Llys quarry
F8	Bryn Llys quarry
F9	Deviation tramway
F10	Deviation tramway
F11	Deviation tramway
F12	Deviation tramway
F13	Deviation tramway — note vertical side embankment
F14	Deviation tramway — note vertical side embankment
F15	Deviation tramway — Chwarel Fawr mill

G1	Horse worked tramway
G2	Deviation tramway
G4	See F4
G6	Deviation tramway
G7	Deviation tramway
G8	Original summit of Chwarel Fawr incline
G9	Route of abandoned Chwarel Fawr incline
G10	Route of abandoned Chwarel Fawr incline
G11	Route of abandoned Chwarel Fawr incline
G12	Drumhouse of truncated Chwarel Fawr incline
G13	Chwarel Fawr incline
G14	Chwarel Fawr incline
G15	Chwarel Fawr incline
G16	Chwarel Fawr incline
G17	Bottom of Chwarel Fawr incline
H1	Bottom of upper section of "village branch"
H2	Levelled area
H3	Levelled area
H4	Levelled area Bus turn round
H5	Allt Ddu engine shed
H17	Bonc Fawr junction with Chwarel Fawr incline
H18	Bottom of Chwarel Fawr incline
I1	Edge of Allt Ddu pit
I2	Levelled area
I3	Levelled area
I4	Road/rail ramp
I7	Deviation tramway
I15	Bottom of Ellis incline
J6	Head shunt, Village tramway
K1	Allt Ddu pit
L1	Allt Ddu pit

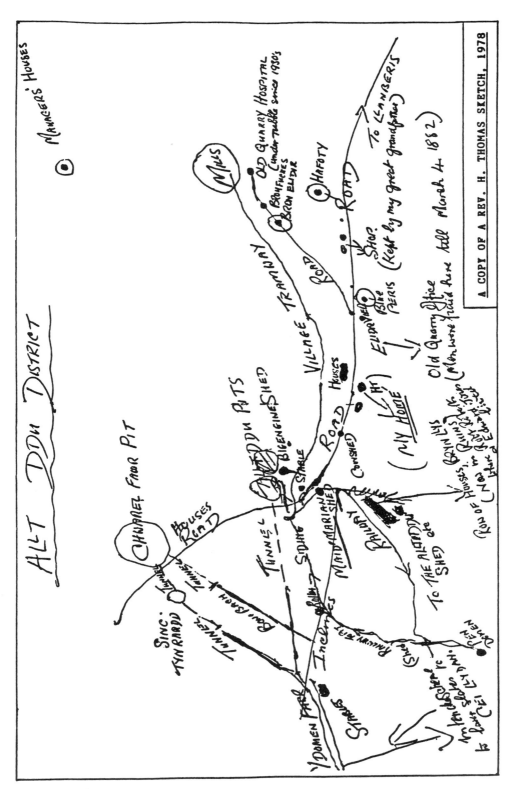

Illus.17

7. The Village or Allt Ddu Branch

It has already been written, that following the construction of the lake-level Padarn Railway and subsequent abandonment of the Dinorwig Railway, it became necessary to provide an alternative means of transporting Allt Ddu and Chwarel Fawr slate to the lakeside. The tempting prospect of a line down the valley of the Afon Fachwen has also been mentioned. There must have been a very good reason why a new inefficient uphill tramway was built in preference to the direct downhill route to Cei Llydan (*wide quay*).

The route adopted was the forerunner of the so-called "Village Branch" and took the form of an uphill link to the main western inclines at "Steam Mills". The tramway commenced at the top of the Chwarel Fawr incline and after a level section of 100 yards (92m), it turned through 90 degrees and immediately started the climb. During the 600 yard (549m) journey the line climbed 60 feet (18m) vertical equivalent, an average gradient of 1 in 30 (3.3%). At the steepest part, the horses and waggons struggled 130 degrees round a granite hillside bluff where the average gradient was 1 in 20 (5%). It is quite remarkable that, for nearly 60 years, the whole of the Allt Ddu — Chwarel Fawr product was hauled by sweating horse power to the summit, 660 feet (201m) above the lake, only to be lowered down to the Padarn Railway at lake level. At a later date, the track became incorporated in the main access road to the quarry 1,000 foot (305m) level. Apart from the bottom few yards which are now landscaped, most of the road is still extant and the gradient experienced. Close to the summit there is still a widened and levelled area, which was probably a storage area and sidings. A similar set of sidings was provided at the bottom of the hill.

It might be helpful to obtain a rough estimate of the traffic on the branch. In a cost estimate[22] for the conversion from horse working to steam locomotive working; a monthly production of 2,300 tons is quoted. It is not stated whether this is an actual or projected figure. For the sake of argument, let us take 1,000 tons per month or 37 tons per working day as reasonable. It is difficult to assess what the "tractive effort" of a horse is, particularly on a hill. However, the author has been advised that a load of two tons would seem to be in the right order. On this basis, it would have been necessary to undertake 18.5 journeys per working day. The congestion would have been considerable, particularly when a "slot" had to be found for the returning empties. If more than 1,000 tons per month were being moved, "double heading" or more horses and waggons would have been necessary. The bottleneck caused by the limitations of the line must have seriously restricted output from Allt Ddu/Chwarel Fawr. Following a strategic re-appraisal of the Allt Ddu problem, which no doubt included another look at the direct downhill route to Cei Llydan, it was decided to construct a completely new uphill branch, along with a new associated tramway in the Allt Ddu/Chwarel Fawr area. This was a narrow gauge construction in the grand manner, undertaken between, 1899 and 1902. Although the new track had severe gradients, there was only one significant bend, and there is little doubt that it was all designed with the steam locomotive in mind. In 1980, the already mentioned, *Bargen Dinorwig* by Emyr Jones was published. This was a prize-winning entry in the 1979 National Eisteddfod, and quotes in some detail the cost of converting the new tramway to locomotive haulage.

The change from horses to locomotive working from Mill to Allt Ddu. 7/1902

Cost of horses. £25 per month	£325 per year.
Est. cost of loco. £10 per month.	£130 per year.
Difference	**£195 per year.**
Monthly tonnage 2,300 tons.	
2,000 yards of new rail at 10/- (50p)	£1,000
New locomotive	£ 550
Locomotive shed	£ 120
New fence by the railway	£ 50
Old Bridge. (too low)	£ 30
Total Cost. Estimate	**£1,750**

(It will be noted that there is no charge for labour.)

Some of the figures are of interest. A monthly tonnage of 2,300 tons amounts to 29,000 tons per year which in 1902, was about one third of the total Dinorwig production. Such a large contribution was a good enough reason for investment in the new track etc. The fact that the cost of conversion from horse to steam appears as a separate charge, suggests that the new formation had already been built and worked by horses.

The 'Village' Tramway,
looking down to Allt Ddu, 1966

The 'Village' Tramway
looking towards 'Mills'.
Snowdon in the background

The purchase of 2,000 yards (1830m) of new rail or 1,000 track yards (915m) indicates that the whole route from the top of the Chwarel Fawr incline to Steam Mills was re-laid in preparation for the steam engine. The reference to "old bridge" is puzzling, there being no obvious bridge shown on the 1888 Plan. A cost of £550 for the new engine is about one twentieth what it would now cost to buy a second-hand one. (1993)

The branch started at a turn-out off the 892 foot (272m) level, Fawr line, 125 yards (114m) west of the Allt Ddu mill. For 110 yards (101m) the track ran parallel to the tip line, climbing slowly on a shallow waste slate embankment, no doubt useful to get up speed for the big climb ahead. Alongside the mill, the gradient steepened and the line veered clockwise before ascending a long anti-clockwise curve, much of it built on a substantial vertical-sided slate block embankment; this was about twenty feet high at the upper end. Continuing the climb over the old Bryn Llys quarry waste tip, the site of the original Chwarel Fawr drumhouse was passed on the left. Following a shallow cutting, the Allt Ddu engine shed was passed on the right side. In a few yards the line levelled and entered a 30 yard (27m) long reverse shunt. At this point the train would have ascended 51 feet during its 1,331 feet (406m) long climb, an average gradient of 1 in 26

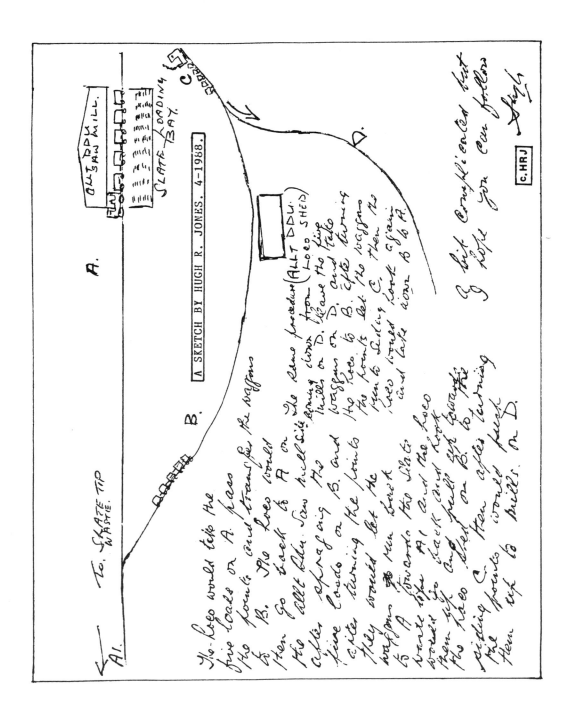

(3.8%). During the short period of horse-working, the horses would have been transferred to the other end of the train, in preparation for the second part of the climb. For much of its length, the upper section was laid on a vertical-sided slate block embankment and a slate block supported shelf cut in the hillside. The average gradient was 1 in 32 (3.1%), but at the steepest part, 1 in 20 (5.0%), it was in close proximity with the earlier line. The track turned through ninety degrees, an unavoidable feature that did nothing to ease the struggle. At the summit, there was a level section which rejoined the original line to Steam Mills. The whole of the second part of the climb was scenically spectacular; after passing through a short wooded section, the magnificent Snowdon panorama burst in to view.

During October 1903, the Hunslet Engine Company despatched two *Velin* (Alice) class engines to the quarry. One of these, No.822 became Dinorwig "No.5", later *Maid Marian*; and the other, No.823 became Dinorwig "No.6", later *Irish Mail*. The two engines were not identical, No.822 was ordered specifically for use on the branch and was fitted with a domed boiler, no doubt, to prevent the boiler priming on the steep climb. No.823 which had the normal domeless boiler, was fitted with a cab. *Maid Marian* went up and down the branch until September 1931, when it was replaced by *Lady Madcap*, second hand Hunslet rather similar to the Penrhyn Quarry "Port Class" engines. It was suitable for the line because it had a domed boiler. In 1952, the "Madcap" was withdrawn from service because the boiler had been condemned. The work at Allt Ddu was taken over by *Velinheli* which, by this time, had acquired the re-conditioned domed boiler from *Maid Marian*. *Velinheli* was to work the branch until April 1959, when it returned to lake level. The now reduced workload on the branch was undertaken by a diesel locomotive. There is an unsupported rumour, denied by the Rev. Thomas, that *Covert Coat* also worked the line, but as this engine did not have a domed boiler its use at Allt Ddu is questionable. However, it is probable that *Maid Marian* carried *Covertcoat* plates for a limited period. (See horse engine names)

The working of the branch is certainly worth describing, it can only be described as incredible. The train or "ryn" was assembled alongside the Allt Ddu mill. When ready, the engine drew the five full waggons over the points at "B". After changing the points the engine propelled the waggons over the points and up the hill for a short distance, where they halted. After spragging the waggons, the engine moved back over the points, leaving the waggons on the bank. The next move was for the points to be changed following which, the engine passed over them on to the mill line. The points were then changed for a third time and following the removal of the sprags, the waggons coasted down the hill and over the points; leaving room for the engine, which arrived after yet another points change. After coupling up, the engine paused in order to get a good head of steam, prior to taking the waggons up the hill to the reverse shunt. When the author first read of these "antics", it was with a feeling of disbelief. The whole procedure was to transfer the engine from one end of the "ryn" to the other. This could have been done quite simply by building a loop round the waggons. (The 1914 O.S. map suggests that such a procedure might have been possible by using a loop through the mill.) Another alternative to the "antics", would have been to *pull* the waggons over the mill line points and *propel* them to the reverse shunt, and then *pull* them to Steam Mills; none of the strange manoeuvres would have been necessary. The author has been assured by Hugh Jones, the ex Chief Engineer that the procedure did occur, and it has also been confirmed by the engine driver. A copy of Hugh Jones's sketch illustrating the events is appended. After a suitable pause in the reverse shunt, getting a good head of steam, the engine propelled the waggons up the hill to Steam Mills. It was fortunate that, at the bottom of the climb, there were about 100 yards (92m) of level track where sidings had been situated during the horse-working days. The respite enabled the engine to rush the bank. The return of the waggons is also of interest. One of the very few photographs of *Lady Madcap* at work, shows it at Steam Mills with about ten "Wagan Llwythwr" in tow. However, it is on record that gravity working was practised on the upper section of the branch[23]. The author is not aware of any waggons fitted with a braking system; perhaps a simple "scotch" was used. The engine escorted the empty waggons down the lower section.

Returning to the estimate of a monthly production of 2,300 tons, this can be restated as 110 tons or 14 round trips per day, assuming that five waggons carried a total of 7½ tons; a lot of work for one engine. The provision of an engine-shed for two engines, gives cause for speculation that two engines might have been available for use, although the author is unaware of any regular standby. A replacement engine would have been essential in the event of a breakdown and during maintenance periods. No engine was normally shedded at nearby Steam Mills. In the absence of a second engine at Allt Ddu, a whole Department could have been isolated until a replacement engine had been transferred from another gallery or brought all the way from Gilfach Ddu. In later years, rail-road ramps were built, one adjacent to the Allt Ddu engine shed and the other at Gilfach Ddu.

On an unknown, but presumably, late date a decision was made to abandon the gwaliau★ system on all levels above "Swallow" (A6T) and process the slate at a central mill. Because Steam Mills could not cope with the workload, slate blocks were taken down the branch to Allt Ddu mill and after processing, the slates were taken back up the hill for lowering to lake level. During these operation a 30 horse-power Ruston and Hornsby diesel locomotive was available to assist with the pushing and pulling. In 1933, the *"Madcap"* fractured an axle on the climb up to Steam Mills and it was replaced, on the spot, by the "flygang" sent up from the workshops, no mean feat.

Considering the exposed location and severe gradients of the Branch, it is surprising that the few photographs of the three engines show them to have no cab or sanding gear; both were standard Hunslet fittings and one is tempted to think that, when the two engines were delivered in 1903, the cab had been fitted to the wrong one. As far as sanders are concerned, the available photographs show the telltale blank bolt holes on the tank where a sander had been fitted at one time. H. A. Jones, has suggested that in the very damp conditions on the mountainside, the sand would not have flowed.

The Branch had a few names, most referring to the village. This is strange; it was not a local name, and in any case, it never went to the village. Perhaps the Allt Ddu Branch would have been a more suitable name.

★ The "gwaliau" (walls) were rows of open fronted slate block huts, where slate was manually processed.

*The four foot gauge Padarn Railway locomotive Dinorwic
pulling a track lifting train, 1962. (N. McNish)*

8. Richard Jones — Dic Bach Dreifar

Retired in 1932 From words recited at his Cyfarfod Ymadawol/Farewell Meeting

Bu yma am flynyddau
Yn gyrru'r injian bach
A'i wyneb fel y fagddu
Ond calon lân ac iach.

Sawl bore du ymlwybrodd
Cyn canu corn y gwaith
Mewn trefn i gael *Maid Marian*
Yn hwylus erbyn saith.

Esgynnai mil o wreichion
I entrych lan y nen
Pan fyddai'r shed yng ngofal
Y dreifar o'r Fachwen.

Bu'n hwylus a llwyddiannus,
Gofalus gyda'r brac
A'i chwiban oedd fyddarol
I deithiwr ar ei drac.

Cyfaill

He was here for many years
Driving his little engine
His face as black as hell
But his heart pure and clean

How many mornings he made his weary way
Before the quarry hooter sounded
To get Maid Marian
Ready by seven

A thousand sparks ascended
Up to high heaven
When the shed was in the charge
Of the driver from Fachwen

He was efficient and successful
And careful with the brake
And his whistle was deafening
To a trespasser on the track.

Friend

Following the purchase of "No.5", Maid Marian in 1903, it was allocated to Allt Ddu and the "Village Branch". Richard Jones was appointed as the regular driver, and remained so until 1932, when the engine returned to Gilfach Ddu for a major overhaul. Richard Jones retired at the same time, due to ill health, after nearly 30 years on the same footplate. The "Meeting" would have taken place in the Allt Ddu "Caban" or hut/canteen, in the presence of his workmates. He was a highly respected and liked gentleman.

A photograph is appended showing Maid Marian in the quarry with Richard Jones on the footplate. He is accompanied by Dafydd Davis, (David Davies), who became a local footballer of some talent.

Maid Marian, probably at 'Australia' CST. c.1936.
The original Type 'B' frames can just be seen at rear

Maid Marian at Pen Garret, 1965. Note the Type 'A' frames

9. Some Notes on the Hunslet Velin-Dinor Class of Engine

Following the delivery to Dinorwig in 1886, of the Hunslet-built locomotive *Velinheli*, some twenty-four similar engines were supplied to the North Wales slate industry. The last one Michael, was delivered to Llanberis in 1932. Of the twenty-four engines, which had the Hunslet code names *Velin and Dinor*, sixteen were delivered to Dinorwig, four to Penrhyn Quarry, three to Pen yr Orsedd and one to Dorothea quarries. Other engines, such as the Penrhyn *Gwynedd* were also delivered, but although having a close family resemblance, they were larger and had design differences, such as stepped frames. However, some of the differences were a result of the various owner's whims and fancies. As far as Dinorwig is concerned, there have been differencies in engines of the Dinorwig "*Alice*" and "*Port*" classes. Of particular interest is the variation of the frame side profile and buffer beams. The author has attempted to categorise them in three groups, including an interesting sub-group of two. Type "A" was established by *Velinheli* and is characterised by the shallow slope frame cut-aways at both the front and rear. Type "B" is similar, but the cut-aways are shorter and at a steeper angle. The third variant, Type "C", has equal depth frames and buffer beams and no cut-aways. Listed below are the twenty-four engines, their frame types and whether they had a dome.

Velin/Dinor Engines in North Wales Slate Quarries

Common Name	Number	Date	Type	Other Info.
Velinheli	409	1886	A	Din.
King/Scarlet	492	1889	B	Din.
Red Damsel	493	1889	A	Din.
Rough Pup	542	1891	A	Din.
Margaret	605	1894	C	Pen.
Alan George	606	1894	C	Pen.
Bernstein	678	1898	C★	Din.★
Covertcoat	679	1898	C★	Din.★
George B	680	1898	B	Din.
Nesta	704	1899	C	Pen.
Elin	705	1899	C	Pen.
Britomart	707	1899	B	P.y.O.
Dorothea	763	1901	B	Dorothea
Holywar	779	1902	B	Din.
Alice	780	1902	B	Din.
Maid Marian	822	1903	A	Din. Dome
Irish Mail	823	1903	B	Din.
Sybil	827	1903	B	P.y.O.
Wild Aster	849	1904	B	Din.
Una	873	1905	B	P.y.O.
No.1	1429	1923	C	Din.Dome
Dolbadarn-	1430	1923	C	Din.Dome
Michael	1709	1932	C	Din.Dome

Din. = Dinorwig   Din.★ = Dinorwig   Type B with deep frames
Pen. = Penrhyn   P.y.O. = Pen yr Orsedd

It can be inferrred that the change in profile from Type "A" to Type "B" was a distinct change in design. On the face of it, the claim would seem to be without foundation. According to the list, two engines were delivered in 1899, *King of the Scarlets* and *Red Damsel*. As the former apparently had Type "B" frames and the latter were Type "A", it was reasonable to assume that both types were established at an early date. In 1891, two more Type "A" deliveries were made. Although the neighbouring Penrhyn Quarry was an early Hunslet customer, it was 1894 before they bought two "Velin" engines, *Margaret* and *Alan George*. Although the events at Penrhyn are really outside the scope of this account, mention must be made of these engines, as they established the full depth Type "C" frames.

In 1896, a major reconstruction of Port Dinorwig was commenced[24] and although there was steam haulage available at the time, two new engines, *The First* and *The Second* were delivered in 1898 to work the amended system. At a later date they were *Bernstein* and *Covertcoat*. It will be seen that these engines had Type "C★" frames, but with a difference. Unlike the later Type "C" engines, the buffer-beams were lower than the frames and the reinforced bottoms were only two inches (51mm) above the rails. They were both fitted with the Hunslet type of twin spring buffer. The order also included a Type "B" engine, latterly known as *George B* which probably worked for a short time at the Port. Penrhyn must have been satisfied with their 1894 purchases, as two more, *Nesta* and *Elin* were acquired in 1899. The four engines comprised the Penrhyn Small Quarry Class. One must assume that the Penrhyn Management were not keen to have a Class name with close Dinorwig conotations. It is very probable that these two engines were built alongside the Type "B" *Britomart*, the first Hunslet bought by Pen yr Orsedd quarry. The engines must have gained a good reputation as in 1901, the Dorothea Company purchased the Type "B" *Dorothea*. Although by 1902 output had fallen, two more engines were obtained by Dinorwig, *Holy War* and *Alice*, both Type "B" versions. By 1903, eleven engines had been acquired since the last Type "A" engine, *Cloister*. Lo and behold, the next two purchases were the apparently Type "A" *Maid Marian* and the Type "B" *Irish Mail*. It is probable that this pair were built alongside No.827, the Type "B" *Sybil*, a second engine for Pen yr Orsedd. To return to *Maid Marian*, this engine was obtained for the so-called Village Branch, which is described in another section. Suffice to say it was steep, and *Maid Marian* was the only Dinorwig *Velin* engine to be fitted with a dome. One is bound to ask, why was a Type "A" ordered for the branch? A Type "B" would have been more suitable, as every bit of extra weight would have been advantageous on the climb; adhesion would have been marginally better. Two more Type "B"'s were delivered to North Wales, No.844 *Wild Aster* for Dinorwig in 1904 and in 1905, the gallery engine, No.873, *Una* for Pen yr Orsedd.

In 1922 the industry was well past its peak, nevertheless, the Company must have been doing reasonably well, as two new engines were delivered by Hunslet. These were not *Velin* engines, but a somewhat updated version of the Type "C". Hunslet used the code-name *Dinor* for these engines. They were locally called the "Port" Class, as they replaced the earlier port engines *Bernstein* and *Covertcoat*, when they were transferred to the quarry. The reason for the purchase of these engines is not clear. *Bernstein* and *Covertcoat* must have been in reasonable condition as they continued to work in the quarry for many years, despite the fact that the deep buffer beams caused difficulties, in fact they would have made good bulldozers. In addition there was difficulty when they were being moved on and off an incline. Prior to the purchase of the new engines, there had been virtually universal availability of spares. When the *Dinor* engines arrived, a new selection of spares would have become necessary. Bearing in mind that the deep frames and buffers were not ideal for quarry use, why were *Bernstein* and *Covertcoat* not left at the Port and new Type "B" engines obtained for the Quarry? In 1932, the final Port Class engine, *Michael*, was purchased, but it never saw service at the Port, it went straight to Lernion at the top of the Quarry. What can be made of this catalogue of events? Another look at the list can be interesting, indeed surprising. It soon becomes obvious that there are two complementary anomalies. First, the listing of No.492, *King of the Scarlets* as a Type "B" and No.822 *Maid Marian* as a Type "A". In both cases, they are the odd ones out. It does not need much speculation to wonder whether there had been a mix-up at some time. The anomalies have been recognised for a long time but Barnes gives an explanation in his article in Llanuwchllyn Express[25]. During overhauls, some 65 years ago, it was convenient to put *Maid Marian*'s top parts on to *King of the Scarlets* bottom parts. And how does Mr Barnes know this? Quite simple, during an overhaul of *Maid Marian* at Bala some years ago, he found 492, *King of the Scarlets*' number stamped on the frames. On having another look at the ex Engineer's records, there is an entry that in February 1928, an ex *Maid Marian* boiler was taken to California for fitting to *King of the Scarlets*.

Some years ago, the author acquired a photograph of *Maid Marian* with domed boiler. It was a small photograph in moderate condition but it was possible to make a reasonable negative and a print is included. Illus.6. With good eyesight and a little imagination, it is just possible to see the Type "B" frames, particularly at the rear. If it is *Maid Marian*; it must have been taken at Allt Ddu before 1928.

The confusion over *King of the Scarletts* and *Maid Marian*'s frames resulted in the latter having a premature Centenary Celebration at Llanuwchllyn in 1989. Red faces all round.

Although not a *Velin-Dinor* engine, it is convenient at this point to mention the Hunslet built engine *Lady Madcap*. This engine was very similar to the Port Penrhyn "Port Class" engines; *Gwynedd* of 1883, *Lilian* of 1883 and *Winifred* of 1885. The three engines were delivered with a stepped frame. In 1910 Dinorwig purchased *Lady Madcap* second hand. Hunslet supplied the step framed engine new, to the Groby Granite Company, Leicestershire in 1896. It was named *Sextus*, it being the sixth engine that Groby had purchased from the Leeds company. In 1910 Groby replaced the engine by another from Hunslet. Although the same gauge, the replacement was an 0-6-0 which, for some unknown reason, retained the name *Sextus*, despite the fact it was Groby's tenth purchase, including a *Nonus*, from Hunslet. It would seem that, like Dinorwig, the Groby Company remained a loyal and satisfied customer of Hunslet.

Dolbadarn, Sinc Fawr 1967, driver: Jack Owen, Bethel
Note the Class 'C' frames and domeless boiler

10. Louisa and "The First Engine to the Top of Braich"

High on the list of Dinorwig puzzles is the enigma of the tiny Hunslet locomotive *Louisa*, delivered to the quarry in 1877. In 1898, it was sold to Glynrhonwy Quarry. *Louisa* was small, even by quarry standards, it being only ten feet (3.05m) long with a weight of 3 tons 6 cwt. (3,5533kg). Boyd[45] has suggested that it was not powerful enough to encourage further orders. Nevertheless, it remained in service, alongside five of the larger *Velin* (Alice) Class engines, until at least 1896. It has been written[26] that *Louisa* was a small version of the *Velin* class, but this is patently not so; on the contrary, *Louisa* influence can be detected in the later *Velin* class of engine.

About this time, the Company acquired a number of vertical boiler engines, almost certainly from the Caernarfon firm of De Winton; a Company well known for the manufacture of marine and slate quarry equipment. Because of the paucity of reliable information about the Dinorwig units, much has to be inferred from similar units elsewhere. However, it is recorded that the names of the four Dinorwig engines were *Harriet*, *Padarn*, *Wellington* and *Victoria*, no doubt after the Departments to which they were originally allocated. There was also *Peris*, this was also a vertical boiler engine, but significantly different from the usual De Winton design. This engine is discussed more fully in a later section.

In the diary of William Morris, un under-manager in the quarry[27], there is an entry dated, 07/03/1878, "First engine to the top of Braich". A copy of the Rev. Thomas's translation of the relevant page is appended. Braich is an imprecise name for a location, but it can be considered to be on the east side of the quarry, 1,600 feet (488m) above sea-level. It became known as *Australia*, possibly in 1902, when the Commonwealth of Australia was created. During the last thirty years of the 19th. Century, the quarry was at its peak. Developments at the highest levels were extensive and the geography changed rapidly. The 1st Edition of the "25 inch" O.S. Plan shows that by 1888, the works above "Australia" had reached a height of 2,300 feet (702m) above sea level. The tramway system was well developed, with continuous runs three quarters of a mile (1.21km) long. The various levels were connected by a series of "tanc" inclines. At this time the eastern (later "C") inclines were the only means of access to the new developments, as the upper west inclines had not been fully developed. This did not come about until the early 20th. century. During the period, a steam engine must have become essential.

"Tanc" inclines were usually built at short steep locations. Unlike conventional inclines, the waggons did not run on their own wheels, but on a level platform which went up and down on a broad gauge track. It is fortunate that a scale diagram of a similar "tanc" incline has survived[28]. Although it is not dated, it is relevant to this discussion as it depicts the drum-house of the incline connecting Lernion, (C8T) and Llangristiolus, (C10) 2,000 feet (610m) above sea level. The gradient is stated to have been 1 in 2.5 (40%) and the platform to be seven feet (2.14m) square. Another incline in the series had a gradient as steep as 1 in 1.9 (53%).

Following the digression, we can now return to *Louisa* and the other engines. During the 1870's, the Company's locomotive experience was limited to the 1870 *Dinorwic* and the De Wintons. In 1877, *Louisa* and *George*, *Dinorwic*'s near twin, arrived on the scene. The essential question is whether any of these engines could have been taken to the "top of Braich"? *Dinorwic* and *George* can be immediately ruled out; with a length of fifteen feet (4.57m) they could not be accommodated on a seven foot (2.14m) transporter; even across the diagonal. As far as the others are concerned, an assessment of the feasability is surprisingly complex. A number of factors are involved, the length of the transporter, in this case seven feet, the gradient, the length and wheelbase of the engine, the depth of the buffer beam and possibly, the height of the chimney and safety-valve exhaust. The principle involved is shown in the diagrams.

First of all, let us consider the De Wintons. Two examples have been considered, a small single cylinder unit now known to have been at Dinorwig in 1876[29]. The late Tom Rushworth derived a drawing[30] and he considered the engine to be ten feet (3.05m) long with a near symmetrical wheelbase of four feet (1.22m). If an engine, ten feet long, is to be carried on a seven feet transporter, it must be positioned with the wheels as close to the outer edge as possible. This would have resulted in an outer edge overhang of about, $(10-4)/2 = 3$ *feet* (0.91m). If the engine had been positioned at the inner edge, or the wheelbase had been greater than four feet, there would have been an inner edge overhang of up to three feet. If the gradient was steep or the buffer beams were deep, there would have been a real risk of a collision with the top wharf, when the transporter started to descend the incline. The bigger, ex Penrhyn Quarry De Winton, *Alan George*, now housed at the

3

Rhag 28. 1870 Damwain angeuol i Humpy Rob Bwlch twrg i
Drain y Chwarel fynd trosto wrth Leeh Fulfran

DEC 28. 1870 Fatal accident to Humpy Rob Bwlch tramy
through the Quarry tram running over him
by Lleeh Fulfran.

Ebrill 3. 1874 Cymanfa Bangor. Tram y Chwarel yn stopio ei mwyn
yr achos. TRAINS Rhad i Gyfanfa.

SEPT
June 3. 76 Bangor Singing Festival. Quarry tram not running for
the sake of the Cause.. Cheap
trams to the Festival. .

Ion 26 1876 Marw yn sydon yn y Car Gwyllt wrth ddod at ei
waith Robt. Wm Roberts, Brynrefail yn 65 ml oed

Jan 26 1876 Robt Wm Roberts of Brynrefail died Suddenly in
the Car Gwyllt whilst coming to work. 65 yrs of age.

Mawrth 7 1878 Locomotive gyntaf Engine gyntaf, dop y Braich

March 7. 1878 First Locomotive engine to the top of Braich.

Hyd 3. 1881 Dwy wagan lwythog yn dod trwy y tyrnout ar Allt
y Teifyn ac yn malurio y balast ar yn Allt.

Oct 3. 1881 Two loaded waggons came through the turnout on
the Terfyn Incline and smashed the ballast on the
Incline

Hyd 6. 1881 Wyth waggon lwythog o lechan o Ben y Garret,
yn ymollwng trwy y tyrnowt yn malurion gân
ddingllo yr allt ar thaffan.

Oct 6. 1881 Five loaded slate waggons from Ben y Garret
ran through the turnout — Smashing
themselves and destroying the incline and
the ropes

'Louisa' circa 1878.
Taken from damaged
plate negatives

Note that an
overhanging vehicle
could collide with
the wharf. 1969

Narrow Gauge Railway Museum, Towyn, has been used as a model to test the suitability of an engine of this type and size. The engine has an over-frame length of 11 feet 2 inches (3.54m) and a wheelbase of 4 feet 4 inches (1.32m). Because the wheelbase is asymmetrical, each end has to be considered separately. It will be seen on the diagram that if the tank end of the engine faces the wharf, there is some risk of collision. If the engine faced the other way, there is no doubt that the deep scoop-shaped buffer beam would have fouled the wharf.

We now return a second time to little *Louisa*, the main subject of this chapter. It will be seen from the diagram, that although the engine had an unsymmetrical frame design, the short wheelbase of three feet ensured that there was no risk of bumping the wharf. The only relevant comment is that it would have been a good idea to remove the highly vulnerable brake rod, the chimney and safety valve outlet, which projected eight feet (2.44m) in the air. They might have bumped the winding drum. At this stage it might be worthwhile to consider how a *Velin* engine would have fared. *Velinheli*, built in 1886, was the first of the Class. It was thirteen feet (3.96m) long with a near symmetrical wheelbase of 3 feet 3 inches (1m). The diagram shows that the frames have been cut away at both the front and rear. It also shows that although it was a bigger engine than *Louisa*, there would have been no difficulty, particularly if the large wood dumb buffers had been removed. Some members of the class had an amended frame profile. e.g. *Holy War*. These have already been discussed more fully in Chapter 9. The later *Port* Class engines, with their deep frames, might have had some difficulty, unless the buffers had been removed. These considerations have been based on strictly theoretical ideas, flat surfaces, well laid track and no rubbish left lying around. Slate quarries were not like that, any imperfection would have increased the chance of a bump. Returning to the 1895 document compiled in connection with performance and cleanliness of a number of the engines. This is now in the care of Gwynedd Archives[31]. It is an abstract of the performance of the engines during 1895, compiled in connection with annual awards for cleanliness and efficiency.

Engine Name	Tons of Slate (S)	Tons of Coal (C)	(S)/(C)	
V *Tramway*	-----	79	----	£1
V *Enid*	94659	50	1893	7/6
V *Alice*	65184	40	1630	7/6
V *No.2*	45561	31	1469	15/-
Louisa	32733	47	696	
Velinheli	49522	52	952	
V *No.1*	44614	37	1206	10/-
V *Wellington*	47744	49	984	7/6

It will be seen in the table that the tons of slate have been divided by the tons of coal. The resulting quotient can be considered to be an approximate specific fuel consumption or thermal efficiency. On the right side of the table is the value of awards given for cleanliness and efficiency. The "V"s on the left side of the table represent the approving initials of Walter Warwick Vivian, the general manager. It is perhaps significant that the drivers of *Louisa* and *Velinheli* received no award, their specific fuel consumptions were the worst, or perhaps the engines were also dirty. Although no tonnages are quoted for the *Tramway* engine, the driver won the top award of £1. As this section was readily accessible to the public, it was no doubt, thought important to ensure a clean and tidy appearance. The performance of *Wellington*, the 25 year old De Winton, is praiseworthy and demonstrates that the Caernarfon built engine was a force to be reckoned with. In present times, the value of the awards might be thought meagre, but when one remembers that a driver's weekly wage was something like 25 shillings (£1.25), it will be appreciated that the awards were of significant value. In addition, there was of course, the prestige that went with winning an award.

Incidentally, in 1890, John Roberts, driving the *Tramway* engine had already won the first prize of twenty-five shillings (1.25) and Evan Evans on *Enid* got the second prize of £1.00. *Louisa*, in third place with Richard Williams got 15/- (75p). The drivers of *Velinheli* and *Alice* were cautioned about the general state of their engines[3]U22. It would seem that the value of the prizes were at the whim of Mr Vivian.

Why was *Louisa* bought? No doubt, there were good and bad points in the design and the latter were not appreciated at the time of purchase. However, the author believes that it was a thought out buy. It could well have been "The first locomotive to the top of Braich" and the ability to take it up and down "tanc" inclines, must have been a paramount consideration. The fact that the later *Velin* Class engines could also be accommodated on "tanc" inclines suggests that Dinorwig and Hunslet engineers co-operated in the design. Of course there was also the ability to steam round short radius bends. Following the introduction of *Velinheli*, Hunslet advertised a smaller *Velin* engine with virtually the same mechanical specification as *Louisa*, the Hunslet code name was *Solia*.

To finish on a whimsical note, the author likes to imagine the time when *Louisa* was the only engine at the "top of Braich". The thought of the engine hauling a load of waggons to the incline and then accompany them up or down, and then repeat the performance on another level, is perhaps not too far-fetched. What a pity the little engine did not survive; it would have been a great favourite at Bala and Llanberis.

Inclines and Engines

Scale 7mm = 1 foot   Gradient A = 1 in 1·9.
                              B = 1 in 2·5.

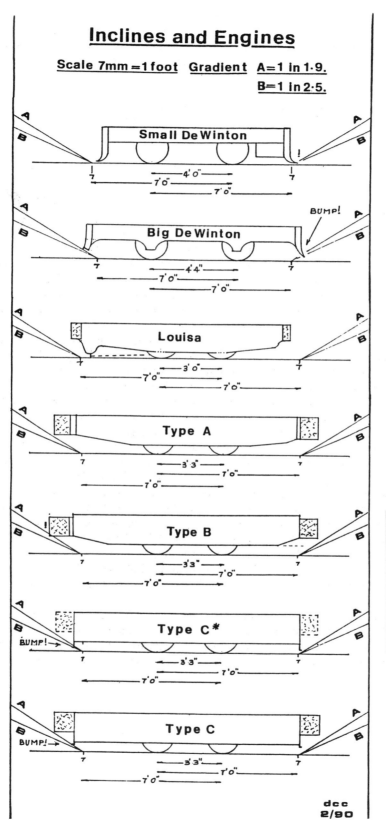

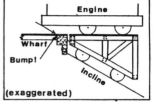

Engine
Wharf
Bump!
Incline
(exaggerated)

"MAIN LINE" TANC INCLINES

I.E. HIGHER THAN AUSTRALIA
C5T 1630 FT. A.S.L.

C6   LENGTH 340 FT. 1 IN 3.6
C7   LENGTH 239 FT. 1 IN 2.6
C8   LENGTH 260 FT. 1 IN 1.9

IT IS NOT CONFIRMED THAT
THESE WERE THE ORIGINAL
TANK INCLINES TO THE
"TOP OF BRAICH"

dcc
2/90

11. The Dinorwig Locomotive Names

If you talk to anybody who claims to know anything about the Assheton Smith family and Dinorwig Quarry, they will probably tell you that it was the place where engines were called after racehorses. Of course, this is correct, but the horses were only one of engine names; others had family, geographical and miscellaneous names. An independent study of each group is not simple; there are cross references and it was not uncommon for names to change. However, for the sake of convenience, the names are discussed under a number of general headings.

The Family Names

On making a start on family names, one soon becomes involved in the family trees of two local "quality" families, the Assheton Smiths of Faenol (Vaynol) Park on the mainland shore of the Menai Strait and the Vivian family of Pentraeth, Anglesey. Apart from the Padarn Railway engines *Fire Queen* and *Jenny Lind*, the first engine acquired by the quarry was the Hunslet engine *Dinorwic* of 1870. It would therefore seem that a study of the family trees prior to that date, would serve no great purpose. A simplified family tree is appended. The second Thomas Assheton Smith, "Tom Smith", inherited the estate from his father, Thomas Assheton Smith in 1828. "Tom Smith", an accomplished steam engineer, died without heir in 1858 and the estate passed to his great nephew, George William Duff, provided he assumed the name Assheton Smith. The narrow gauge Hunslet engine No.184 of 1877 was called *George* after him. In 1888 George married Laura Alice Stanhope Jones, who in 1889 had an engine *Alice* named after her. After the marriage, this lady's initials formed the acronym *Ladas* which can be found in a number of quarry connotations. It was also the name of the ill-fated Snowdon Mountain Railway engine that derailed on the Opening Day, with disastrous consequences. George and Laura had a daughter, Enid who gave her name *Enid* to *S.M.R.* No.2 and the quarry engine, Hunslet No.493 of 1889. (The *S.M.R.* was built on Faenol property.) When George died in 1904, the estate passed to his brother, Charles Garden Duff, who also assumed the Assheton Smith name. In 1911 he was created a Baronet. Charles was the source of the name *Charlie*, Hunslet No.51 of 1870, previously called *Dinorwic*. The change probably occured in 1882, when Hunslet No.302 was acquired for the Padarn Railway. It was, no doubt, considered to be more worthy of such a prestigeous name than a mere quarry engine. Sir Charles married three times, the first time in 1876 to Lady Maud Francis of the Vivian family. Her brother, Walter Warwick Vivian, was General Manager of the quarry for 22 years. There was a son of the marriage, Robert George Vivian Duff, who did not adopt the Assheton Smith name. He inherited the estate in 1914, but within three weeks he was killed in the 1914-18 war. The estate then passed to his son Charles Michael Robert Vivian Duff, who in 1932, gave the name *Michael* to Hunslet No.1709 of 1932. Sir Michael married Hon. Joan Marjoribanks, daughter of Lord Tweedsmouth, and, for some time, the Port Dinorwig engine "No.1" was called *Lady Joan*. Sir Michael died in 1980 without an heir and the Baronetcy became extinct.

Returning to Charles, his second marriage was to Mary Elizabeth Brinsley and in 1902, he married a third time, this time to Sybil Mary Verschoyle. In 1906 the new Bagnall engine, No.1760, was named *Sybil* in honour of that lady. Returning again to Robert George, he had a son Henry who, apart from selling some land for the Snowdon Mountain Railway, does not seem to have influenced the railway scene to any great extent. He did have the name Assheton Smith, but this time it was a Christian name. Robert and Mary also had a daughter, Louisa Alice and it was this lady who gave her name to *Louisa*, Hunslet No.195 of 1877. Louisa married the third Lord Vivian. In 1898 *Louisa* was sold to Glynrhonwy Quarry and took the name with her. When Hunslet No.780 was acquired in 1902, it received the name *Alice*, the second name of Louisa Alice. Thus, there were two engines called *Alice*, not the same lady, but sisters in law. There remains one other engine to be mentioned. In 1874 a further engine was acquired, probably a De Winton, and it received the family name, *Harriet*. This lady, who was the sister of "Tom Smith", must have been born about 1830. However, the engine was not named directly after her. It was a geographical name from the Harriet Department, to which it had been allocated.

It might be thought strange that there was not a quarry engine called *Ladas* but, as with ships, after the Snowdon accident, it might have been thought bad luck or insensitive to use the name again.

It is amazing that in 1895, a regatta at Sunderland Point, a remote, tide isolated hamlet on the north Lancashire coast, (SD 427561) was won by a boat called *Ladas*[33]. The boat was owned by a James Gardner.

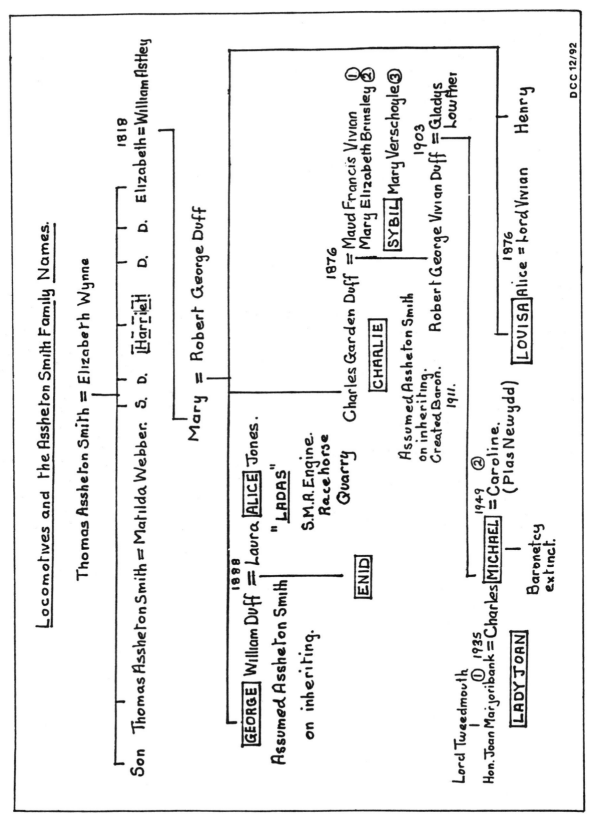

Locomotives and the Assheton Smith Family Names.

Thomas Assheton Smith = Elizabeth Wynne

Son   Thomas Assheton Smith = Matilda Webber.   S.   D.   D.   D.   Elizabeth = William Astley
1818

Mary = Robert George Duff

GEORGE William Duff = Laura ALICE Jones.
1888
Assumed Assheton Smith
on inheriting.

"LADAS"

S.M.R. Engine.
Racehorse
Quarry

ENID

Charles Garden Duff = Maud Francis Vivian ①②
1876   Mary Elizabeth Brinsley ②
                          SYBIL Mary Verschoyle ③
CHARLIE

Assumed Assheton Smith
on inheriting.
Created Baron.
1911.

1903
Robert George Vivian Duff = Gladys
Lowther

LOVISA Alice = Lord Vivian
1876   Henry

Lord Tweedmouth
              ① 1935
Hon. Joan Marjoribank = Charles MICHAEL
LADY JOAN

1949 ②
= Caroline.
(Plas Newydd)

Baronetcy
extinct.

A related Gardner, Tom, had three daughters, the eldest being christened "Ladas". A surviving youngest daughter can recall a racehorse with that name. Perhaps Tom had a good day at the races, and celebrated the event by naming his new daughter after the horse. To date, (1993), no connection has been found.

Addendum

After this section was completed, the author's wife, a crossword enthusiast was studying "Brewer's Dictionary of Phrase and Fable" and came across the entry "Ladas . . . Alexander's messenger, noted for fleetness of foot." Lord Roseberry's horse *Ladas* won the flat Derby in 1894; whereas the Assheton Smith *Ladas* was a steeplechaser.

The Padarn Railway Engine Names

The four foot gauge Padarn Railway's first steam locomotives were the Horlock built *Fire Queen* and *Jenny Lind*. They were delivered to Llanberis in 1848. Where did such a splendid name as *Fire Queen* originate? It was certainly not a local name. One has to go to Clydeside for an answer. In 1839 Robert Napier, a Glasgow shipbuilder, built the 281 g.t. *Fire King* for the Ardrossan — Liverpool service. The second Thomas Assheton Smith ("Tom Smith"), who was an accomplished steam engineer in his own right, was closely associated with Robert Napier on various projects, including a number of steam yachts. Jaggers[34] tells a nice little story about the yachts being called *Fire King*, and that in honour of Queen Victoria, a superior vessel was called *Fire Queen*. Whether the story is true or not, does not really matter, but it did provide an excellent name for the first Dinorwig steam locomotive. Incidentally, there was a Clydeside vessel named *Fire Queen* in commercial service by 1879.

Jenny Lind, the "Swedish Nightingale", was a very popular opera singer who made her first appearance on the London stage in 1847. She made a great impact and as well as the Padarn Railway *Jenny Lind*, there was the famous 2.2.2 engine built by Hunslet in 18xx for the London, Brighton and South Coast Railway. Although having the same name, the Leeds engine had a more advanced and successful design, many similar engines were produced. Bearing in mind that the Horlock's were marine engineers, it is strange that Assheton Smith's marine engineering associates on the Clyde, were not entrusted with the building of the first Padarn Railway engines. What a pity there was not a *Fire King* and *Fire Queen*, both names would have been ideal for a pair of engines of usch majestic appearance. Because of the non-standard design of the Horlock engines, it must have been necessary for all spare parts to be specially made.

In 1882, a replacement for *Jenny Lind* arrived from Hunslet. This engine, the first of three, was based on an established standard gauge design. No doubt, spares would have been easier to obtain. It has already been written, that this engine purloined the name *Dinorwic* from the first Hunslet engine delivered to the quarry. In 1882, the second replacement engine arrived. No.410 *Pandora*, although in 1909 the name was changed to *Amalthaea*. The third engine, No.631 *Velinheli* arrived in 1895. The two names *Dinorwic* and *Velinheli* are logical. The third name, *Pandora* is illogical and inconsistent. The similarity between *Pandora* and Padarn is striking, indeed the latter would have been a highly eligible name. In the late Tom Rolt's "A Hunslet Hundred", a book commissioned by Hunslet to mark the Company's centenary, the engine is referred to as *Padarn*. A specific enquiry to the Company, has confirmed that the name in their records is *Pandora*. However, it is easy to speculate that something went wrong with the order; perhaps some bad handwriting. With regard to *Amalthaea*; the name has mythological origins. In more recent times the name was used for one of the planet Jupiter's moons. Incidentally, *Amalthaea* was also the name of an Assheton Smith private yacht[35].

As well as delivering slate via the standard gauge railway connection from Port Dinorwig Quay to the Chester and Holyhead Railway; the Company also owned and operated a number of steam coasters. These delivered Dinorwig slate to ports in the British Isles and occasionally in northern Europe. The names of some of the ships were the same as carried on the railway engines; *Dinorwic, Vaynol, Velinheli, Enid* and *Elidir*.

Racehorse Engine Names

The Faenol (Vaynol) racehorses are remembered for two things, their successes in the Grand National, and the horse names used on the quarry engines. The Assheton Smith family had long been interested in horses and "Tom Smith", who inherited the estate in 1869, was a celebrated foxhunter. His great nephew and heir

VAENOL HORSES – DINORWIC ENGINES

HUNSLET				First Race	Last Race	Active Days	No. of races	Placings				Notes
No.	Date	First Name	Horse Name					1st	2nd	3rd	A.R.	
542	8-91	Nº2	Cloister							1		2nd in 1891 G.Nat. for Lord Dudley / 2nd in 1892 G.Nat. 1st in 1893 G.Nat.
671	5-98	Port Dinorwic	Cackler	7.02.08	2.03.11	1118	8	7		1		
638	9-95	Vaenol	Jerry M	26.03.08	29.03.11	1464	8	7	1	1	1	1st in 1912 G.National.
779	5-02	Nº3	Holy War	30.03.08	31.12.10	1006	10	5	3	1	1	
541	6-91	Nº1	Rough Pup	5.01.10	21.01.10	16	3		1	1	2	
			Indian Runner	10.03.11	1.08.11	143	3		1	1	2	Nameplate pattern found.
652	--96	Elidir*	Lady Madcap	22.04.11	26.04.13	728	10	3	2	2	5	Bought secondhand 1910. Previously "Sextus"
			Master Mine	22.04.11	24.03.13							
			Broadstrother	18.04.11	?							
679	11-98	The Second	Covert Coat	11.11.11	27.03.14	867	14	3	2	2	7	1st in 1913 G.National
			Brasslock	12.01.12	16.02.12	35	2	2		1		Nameplate pattern found.
492	11-89	Alice	King of the Scar.	2.12.11	8.02.13	434	9	1	1	1	7	
			Flaxen	26.10.12	25.10.13	366	10	2	2	2	4	Nameplate pattern found.
			Flaxseed	8.02.13	7.11.13	244	3		2	2	3	Nameplate pattern found,
678	8-98	The First	Bernstein	5.03.13	16.03.14	378	5	4			1	
849	6-04	Nº7	Wild Aster	6.01.14	13.04.14	60	2	1	1			
184	--87	George	Minstrel Park	11.01.13	13.04.14	460	9	6	?	?	2	
680	--98	Wellington	George B	17.01.14	13.04.14	86	9	0	?	?	2	
493	10-99	Enid	Red Damsel	7.01.14	6.03.14	48	11	1			10	
823	10-03	Nº6	Irish Mail	25.10.13	19.12.13	55	2	1				
			Formelhaut	25.10.13	19.12.13		3	1	1		1	
822	10-03	Nº5	Mad Marian	20.12.13	27.12.13	7	2	2				1st in 1914 G.Nat. Bought by Sir Charles
			Sunlock	Did not acquire a horse name.								D.A.S. after the race. Sir Charles died 9.1914. By 12.1914 raced by W.W.Vivian
780	6-02	Nº4	Alice	Did not acquire a horse name.								Quarry Manager.

Nameplate patterns on quarry made cast ironframes.
Gilfach Ddu. 1966

George William Duff was also a keen horse man. His brother Charles Garden Duff, who succeeded him in 1904, was an enthusiastic owner and Grand National winner. It is said that he did not get on well with the rest of the family, and that he would have had little hesitation in exchanging the engine family names for horse names. At the time of Queen Victoria's Diamond Jubilee in 1887, George William had planted many trees on the Foel Rhiwen hillside (581644) to form the word "Jubilee". Charles, who was normally a kindly man, must have had a vindictive streak, as when he inherited the estate he had the trees removed, they were brother George's idea. Nevertheless, it is this gentleman who we must thank for so many of the splendid Dinorwig engine names.

There is little doubt that the first Dinorwig engine to acquire a horse name was Hunslet No.542 of 1891, number-named "No.2". In 1891, a horse called "Cloister" was second in the Grand National for Lord Dudley. After the race it was purchased by Charles and in 1892, it was again second in the Grand National. The following year it won the Grand National for Charles. This presents a little query. Did George change the name of *HE* 542 from "No.2" to that of his brother's horse or did he wait until 1894, when he inherited the estate, before calling the engine *Cloister*? Although Charles continued to be keen on steeplechasing, it was to be six years before another engine received a horse name. However, there was soon to be a big change. In the period, February 1908 to December 1913, at least twenty horses were acquired, many with names still recognised to this day on a number of narrow gauge railways. It is commonly believed that an engine gained a horse name in order to commemorate a particular horse or event. Can this be substantiated?

A table compiled from newspaper records is appended listing the horses in order of acquisition and the performance of the corresponding racecourse. The table also shows engine numbers and dates relative to the horses. The dates of acquisition are not included; as it would seem that the period between first and last races would be of more significance. It would have been then when a nameplate would be earned; an "active period", ranging from 1,464 days for *Jerry M* to a mere seven days for *Maid Marian*. Equally surprising is the number of races run by each horse. *Jerry M* ran eight races in the 1,464 day long active period and *Red Damsel*, which ran eleven races in a 51 day period. What about the race placings? There was a nameplate for *Rough Pup*, which did not have first place but apparently nothing for *Flaxen* which had two "firsts" and two "seconds". Similarly, *Brasslock* got two "firsts" in only two outings and nothing else. The list includes three Grand National winners, *Cloister*, *Covert Coat* and *Jerry M*. All three names appeared on nameplates.

It is now (1993) nearly ninety years since these events occurred, and after such a long time it is difficult to comprehend the situation at the time. The idea of calling an engine after a meritorious racehorse is certainly attractive, but the poor performance of *George B* would seem to negate the proposition. The position of *Maid Marian* is curious. The record shows that on January 12/12/1913 it was running for a Mr Tabor. On 20 and 27/12/1913 it ran for Sir Charles and following two wins it did not appear again in the calendar. By

January 1915, it had been acquired by a Mr Platt. On 7/1/1914 *Red Damsel*, on its first time out for Sir Charles got a first place. It ran a further ten races for Charles but did not have another win. In the table there are four horses, *Indian Runner, Brasslock, Flaxen* and *Flaxseed*. These horses ran for Sir Charles and one of them, *Brasslock* had two wins in two appearances. Nameplate patterns for the four names were found in a quarry store shortly before closure. Although there is no evidence of them being used, there is none to the contrary. Returning to *Red Damsel* and *Maid Marian*, the fact that they had racehorse names suggests that despite the poor showing of the former and the short stay of the latter, only seven days; they acquired the names before race-day and that the names were cast and fitted immediately after the horse was purchased. This would not have been too difficult as the patterns were made from pre-fabricated bases and "tack-on" letters. As there was a brass foundry at Gilfach Ddu, the casting could have been done without delay.

In 1914 Sir Charles died and the estate was inherited by his son Robert George who, within days, was killed in the Great War. The estate passed to his son Michael; the short but glorious racehorse era had come to a sudden end. The horse names we know today are as frozen in 1914. Apart from one case, there is little evidence of an engine having more than one horse name. The exception is "No.5". There is evidence that it was called *Covert Coat* prior to *Maid Marian*, i.e. during the period between the first race of the former and the first race of the latter. In 1978 the author was fortunate to have discussions with the Rev. Herbert Thomas, great-grandson of the great Griffith Ellis, general manager of the quarry in the mid. 19th century. As a child he lived about 100 yards (92m) from the Allt Ddu engine shed and he is in no doubt, that between 1912 and 1914, there was an engine called *Covert Coat* at work on the Allt Ddu branch. After all, it had just won the Grand National.

There are other names on the list, and no doubt some forgotten ones. The author has seen references to *Gloria* and *Charlie Peace*. In addition there is *Sunlock*. This horse was bought by Sir Charles after it had won the 1914 Grand National. A nameplate was available for it. Although Sir Charles was to die in a matter of months, there is no reason why there could not have been an engine bearing that name. The records show that it was acquired by W. W. Vivian, the General Manager, and that it ran in his colours.

Although not of strict quarry or railway interest, the origins of some of the racehorse names are worth recording.

Wild Aster by Victor **Wild**	out of **Asteria**
Cackler by **Hackler**	out of Circe
Holy War by **St.** Gris	out of **Carnage**
King of the Scarlets by **Red Prince**	out of St. Bridgid
Maid Marian by **Little John**	out of the **Holy** One
Irish Mail by Kings **Messenger**	out of Betsy **Shannon**
Minstrel Park by Bushy **Park**	out of **Minstrel** Girl

The Geographic Engine Names and Allied Topic

As well as the geographic names *Dinorwic* and *Velinheli* previously mentioned, there were, indeed still are, names having a geographical origin. During the 1870's, it is probable that the De Winton company of Caernarfon supplied a number of their vertical boiler engines to the quarry. (See Peris chapter). Although records are far from complete, it is generally believed that five engines were supplied. All these engines had location names in the sense that they originated from the names of "departments" in the quarry, although they did not necessarily have a geographic origin. e.g. Victoria. *Wellington* arrived in 1870, followed by *Harriet* in 1874, *Peris* in 1875 and *Victoria* in 1876. There was also *Padarn*, but its delivery date is uncertain. About this time, the quarry was at its peak and records indicate that there was only one other engine available, *Dinorwic* of 1870. All the engines must have been hard pressed to cope with the work, particularly at times of maintenance and overhaul. The author believes that another engine was available, and there is some circumstantial evidence in support. It has already been mentioned under another heading, that William Morris, an overseer, wrote in his diary (7/3/1878), that the first steam locomotive was working "at the top of Braich", later "Australia". Almost certainly, the engine referred to would have been a De Winton or the little Hunslet *Louisa* (1877). As the name of the department was Braich, consistency would suggest that the engine would have had the geographic name *Braich*.

In 1886, Hunslet delivered another engine. This was *Velinheli*, the prototype of Hunslet's numerous "Velin" class. Velinheli means "salt water mill", a type of mill powered by the rise and fall of the tide.

Following *Velinheli*, the two family name engines, *Alice* (King of the Scarlets) and *Enid* (Red Damsel) were delivered in 1889, followed in 1891 and 1892 by the "number names", "No.1" (Rough Pup) and "No.2" (Cloister). Three years later Hunslet supplied an engine, the mis-spelled *Vaenol* after the nearby Assheton Smith home. In 1898, no less than four new engines arrived from Leeds, *"The First"* (Bernstein) and *"The Second"* (Covert Coat) for use at the Port. A third one, a new *Wellington*, is also said to have gone there. A fourth engine, similar to *Vaenol*, was place-named *Port Dinorwic* (Cackler), a name that needs no explanation.

If all the above engines were at the Port at the same time, the tracks must have been congested. Is there an explanation of this state of affairs? Probably yes, let us consider *The First* and the *The Second*. Both the engines were a development of the Velin class, but now fitted with full depth frames and buffer beams having a central twin-spring buffer. There are early photographs showing both engines on the quayside. Turning now to *Vaenol* and *Port Dinorwic*; apart from a stepped frame and a cab as standard, these engines, which are still extant, can be considered to be larger versions of the Velin class. The names geographic *Vaenol* and *Port Dinorwic* suggest that despite their size, they were intended for work at the port.

It has already been written that in 1898, the De Winton engine *Wellington* was disposed of. A replacement Hunslet engine was purchased at the same time and inherited the name *Wellington*. This was a shallow frame "velin" engine. Although no written record has been found, it would seem very likely that when delivered, *Velinheli*, would have gone straight to the port; the name demanded it. Thus, there was a situation where four engines could have been seen on the quayside. Yes, it must have been crowded.

During 1897/8, the major re-construction of Port Dinorwic was undertaken; this included the building of a sea-lock and dry dock[24]. It is very likely that the four engines were involved in this work. The construction of the dry-dock would have required a lot of earth removal. On completion, there would have been a surplus of engine power. *Vaenol* and *Port Dinorwic* were transferred to the quarry, for work on the one mile long, Peris-Padarn tramway. At the same time, *Wellington* also went to Llanberis to take up the work it was originally purchased for.

There are three more engines which had a local name during their years at Dinorwig. The first one was Hunslet No.652 of 1896. It was purchased by the Groby Granite Company who named it *Sextus*. In 1910, it was sold to Dinorwig, who renamed it *Elidir*, this being the name of the mountain that Dinorwig and Penrhyn quarries were trying to remove. The engine retained the name until the racehorse period when, in 1911, it was renamed *Lady Madcap*. A further secondhand engine was acquired in 1949. This time it was not built by Hunslet, but by Avonside of Bristol, No.2071 of 1933. On arrival at Llanberis, the name *Elidir* was re-introduced for it. In the 13th. century, a Welsh prince built a castle on a knoll at the south-east corner of Llyn Padarn. The castle was called Dolbadarn, which in English means "Padarn meadow". Remains of the castle are still a prominent landmark. When the Port Class engine "No.2" was transferred from Port Dinorwig to the quarry in 1936, it was imaginatively re-named *Dolbadarn*.

12. Cei Llydan

A ride on the Padarn Lake Railway from Gilfach Ddu, Llanberis to the other end of the lake and back, is one of the most beautiful and evocative train rides in Britain. The ride is along part of the route of the four foot gauge railway which carried Dinorwig slate to the coast for nearly 120 years. The engine pulling the train could well be a genuine Dinorwig one, albeit of narrower gauge. However, the journey was not always as tranquil as today's ride. At the turn of the century, about one mile from Gilfach Ddu (576612), there was considerable quarrying activity. The work expanded and declined rapidly over a period of less than twenty years. Today, nature has camouflaged much of the site and one is left with the questions, what happened and why?

When constructed in the early 1840's, the Padarn Railway closely followed the north-east shore of Llyn Padarn. As far as Penllyn (560625), it was backed by the steep Alltwen and Fachwen hillsides. In order to avoid the blasting of a shelf in the hillside, a slate slab embankment was built in Llyn Peris. (There are very few references to blasting and explosives in the construction accounts). About 1,000 yards (915m) from Gilfach Ddu, the comparitively wide valley of the Afon Fachwen rolls down to the water's edge and in this

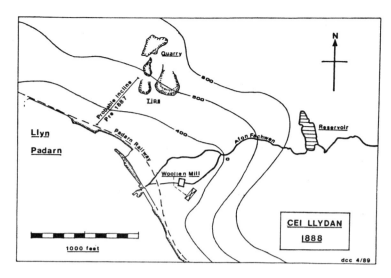

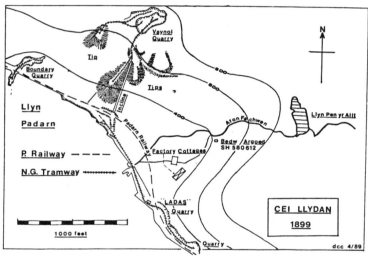

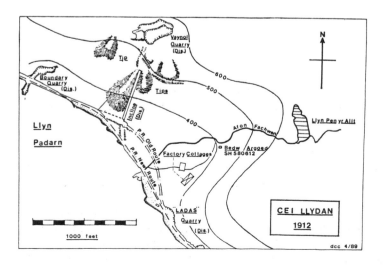

situation, it was relatively easy to lay the line on a shallow embankment round the "bay". At the north-west end of the bay, the line reverted to a lakeside embankment.

The situation in 1888 is shown in Plan "A". The route round the bay can be seen, as well as the remains of an incline from the long abandoned Shelton and Greaves (Vaenol) quarry. The incline was about 150 yards (137m) long, with a gradient of 1 in 3 (33%). Of particular interest, is the nearly completed embankment and the filling in of the enclosed area as the project proceeded. There is also the start of a similar embankment at the bottom of the old incline. This embankment could well have originated as a wharf for the boats taking slate away from the quarry. In the light of future developments, the clean straight edge of the slate embankment is worthy of comment.

Eleven years later, the Second Edition of the Ordnance Survey (Plan "B" shows developments which are immediately obvious. It will be seen that the embankment round the bay had been completed, although the Padarn Railway was still functioning along the original route. During the eleven years, the abandoned quarry had been reopened and a new incline built. By this time, the quarry had acquired the prestigious name of Faenol, the Assheton Smith estate. The map also shows some narrow gauge tramway in the quarry and also in Boundary Quarry, about 250 yards (229m) further along the line. Surprisingly, completely new quarries have been opened up close to the south-east end of the deviation. Although these quarries are not large, the biggest one has the prestigious name of *Ladas*. Both *Ladas* and a nameless new excavation were the start of a narrow gauge tramway, that crossed the Padarn Railway, prior to running along the whole length of the embankment, a total distance of some 400 yards (366m). A couple of short spurs are shown, leading to the embankment wall, which at this stage, still retained a clean straight edge. The small flannel factory shown on the earlier map has become a group of cottages. Some 400 yards (366m) west of Boundary Quarry, the track bed of the Padarn Railway has been widened by cutting into the rock hillside. Generally speaking, the whole area under discussion became known as Cei Llydan (*wide quay*). (Could it have originated from "widened quay"?). After another thirteen years, a further edition was published, the so called 1914 Edition. (Plan "C"). It soon becomes obvious that the changes are as striking as on the 1899 plan. As expected, the Padarn Railway has been relaid along the embankment. The Boundary, *Ladas* and Faenol quarries have been abandoned and virtually all signs of the narrow gauge tramway have vanished. The sharp edge to the embankment is no longer shown, and large tonnages of slate have been pushed over the edge into the lake, so much so, that the original wall is situated some 15 feet (4.6m) from the water's edge. On both the 1899 and 1914 editions, a building is shown close to where the tramway crossed the "main line".

Before discussing what happened at Cei Llydan, a description of the present-day scene could be useful. After leaving the Gilfach Ddu terminus, the train steams through the old quarry yard, and after passing under Vivian Arch, there is a surprise view of the expanse of Llyn Padarn. The railway embankment, built in the lake, can be seen for nearly a quarter of a mile (403m) until it disappears round a bend close to *Ladas* quarry. A number of small quarries are passed but these are mere scratchings, compared with other excavations in the district. Some of the small quarries are not shown on the 1888 plan. After passing *Ladas* quarry, which is quite a small affair, the original route can be seen curving away on the right hand side. The Lake Railway, after passing over a cattle-grid continues on to the deviation. The slate block building, mentioned earlier, is passed on the left side although it is now without door and windows, it is still in reasonable condition. The building contains two rooms, complete with fireplace, and it is plain that one of them housed the controls of a weigh-bridge on the narrow gauge track. The author wonders why it was necessary to weigh rubbish? (H.A. Jones has suggested that the workers were paid on a "weight moved" basis, whether it be slate or rubbish). The original slab edging can still be seen, but the huge quantities of slate waste dumped over the edge make a somewhat derelict scene. On the land side, the area between the original and deviation routes has been partly filled in, although the landside wall can still be seen standing about five feet (1.5m) above the immediate surroundings. Half way along the deviation, the Afon Fachwen is crossed, and after passing a slate waste jetty on the left, the remainder of the deviation can be seen in more or less original form. The original wall can be seen standing in the lake, little rubbish has was dumped at this point. At the north-west end, the 1842 course is rejoined and after a short distance, the widened section is reached. The original 1840 course can be followed and at one point, 30 yards (27.4m) from the water's edge, there are remains of the original wall. The rather cramped area at the foot of the Faenol incline is recognisable but the incline itself is now in a ruinous state, particularly the upper part. At the summit of the incline there are a couple of "domen" from which there is a magnificent view. There are also the remains of a

Cei Llydan 1993. Note the original slate blockwall and waste material dumped over the edge. 1888-1899

Cei Llydan. The weighbridge on the n-g. track

"gwaliau" of seven, right in the centre of a "settlement" of old caravans and "bangers". (1993)

Who would have thought that 75 years after it was superseded, the original course would have become a deviation? In 1974, cables from a pumped storage power station, being built inside Elidir mountain, were buried alongside the railway. As there was no road access to the north-east side of the lake, the railway was intensively used to transport the massive cables and other construction materials. Today, there is little evidence of the colossal job undertaken by the little railway.

What was the reason for the amazing events described? First of all, when did they occur? Boyd writes that the deviation was built during 1914-18 to improve the alignment[36]. Jaggers[37] claims that it was engineered in the early 1900's. However, the Ordnance Survey "25 inch" plan of 1886, shows that the deviation was already 80% complete. Was the re-alignment of the 1841 route necessary? It would seem that it might not have been. As built, the track had a radius of curvature of 222 yards (203m). Although this was a curve of

Overbridge on the track from Vaynol quarry to the incline summit

some consequence, it was by no means unique on the Padarn Railway, there being bends at Penscoins (536678) of 207 yards (189m) radius and a short bend at Lon Las (533643) of 172 yards (157m) radius. At the point where the deviation rejoined the original route, the radius was 246 yards (225m). These radii have been computed from the "25 inch" plan. As these comparitively tight bends were still in use up to the closure of the railway, the reason for the re-alignment is not clear. Although not seriously suggested, it could have been to reduce the drag on the long curve. It would seem that the Horlock engines, which had a wheelbase of twelve feet (3.7m), had no great difficulty operating round the bend for 34 years, when "*Fire Queen* was replaced by *Dinorwic*. The six coupled engine with a wheelbase of ten feet (3.1m) certainly had no difficulty.

Where did the material for the deviation come from? It has been suggested that it was from Faenol, Boundary and *Ladas* quarries[38]. This would seem to be open to question; as already mentioned, the deviation was near to completion before Faenol was developed and *Ladas* opened up. One can hardly imagine that prestigious names like *Vaynol* and *Ladas* would be wasted on rubbish producing quarries. The names would surely be reserved for something much grander. When first built, the deviation was something of a Rolls Royce job. Unlike the L.N.W.R. embankment, on the other side of the lake, the quarry version was built with vertical slate block sides. Between verticals, it was as wide as 35 feet (10.7m). It was a major construction, much bigger than necessary for a simple four-foot gauge railway.

The narrow gauge track shown on the second survey is of interest. Although the survey was done in 1899, it is obvious that the tramway could have been built any time after completion of the 1888 survey. At this time considerable tonnages had been pushing the embankment out across the "bay". Some of the material, at the north-west end could have come from the predecessor of Faenol Quarry, but the great bulk must have come along the Padarn Railway from the main quarry. If so, the first track on the embankment would have been a four foot gauge siding off the main railway. At this time, the quarry would be approaching its maximum output and the necessity to "slot in" works trains and provide engine power and waggons, must have been inconvenient. It could be, that to alleviate the situation, the opening of the local diggings was undertaken. Were narrow gauge locomotive/s used on the deviation? The answer is almost certainly yes, although the plans do not give and indication of an engine shed and no remains are apparent. In the 1870's a number of vertical boiler engines were purchased and one of these is known to have been called *Padarn*. As it was the Company's policy to name engines after the Department to which they were allocated, it can be speculated with some confidence that one of the engines, bearing the name *Padarn*, worked on the deviation. It certainly reinforces the rumour that in 1898, Dinorwig sold a De Winton engine called *Padarn* to Glynrhonwy Quarry on the other side of the lake[39]. This would be just about the time the embankment was completed.

Although the author is unable to explain the mystery of Cei Llydan, it could have been part of a grand plan, which was never completed. This will be discussed in a later section.

13. The Dinorwig De Winton Engines and "Peris"

It is strange, that although Dinorwig purchased a "de Winton" vertical boiler engine as early as 1870; some five years before Penrhyn, very little is known about the Dinorwig units. Seven Penrhyn ones are mentioned in the 1946 book, "Narrow Gauge Railways in North Wales" by Charles Lee, but he makes no reference to any at Dinorwig. The first edition of Bradley and Hindley's famous Pocket Book F was published in 1950. This was followed in 1968 by the second edition, in which a vertical boiler engine named *Wellington* is listed as a "de Winton" with question mark. It was not until the quarry closed in 1969 that additional information gradually came to light. Among the relics that survived was a quarry valuation of 1877, which included three engines *Harriet*, *Peris* and *Victoria*. It has been suggested with little evidence, that these were vertical boiler engines built by de Winton[40]. It is also known that there was another called *Padarn*; and the author has suggested that a case can be made for one called *Braich*. In Boyd's 1986 book, there is a photograph of *Wellington*[41] with a caption stating that it was a de Winton. This could well have been the case, but recently evidence has come to light which suggests that it might not have been.

During 1990, the author was pleasantly surprised to receive two photographs of a vertical boiler engine, one a three quarter view showing the name *Peris*. (A) The second photograph (B), shows a full side view of what is probably the same engine. At least the crew is the same. It is not often that a valuable relic is "discovered" hanging on a pub wall; in this case the *Vaynol Arms* at Nant Peris. Fortunately, the glass negatives are still extant and the author is indebted to Emlyn Bayliss, the landlord, and Tony Coultiss, who supplied the author with copies of the two photographs. Unfortunately, the quality is poor and very contrasty, no doubt due to the ravages of time and poor storage conditions. Nevertheless, this in no way detracts from their value. Copies of the two prints are appended. Following a casual glance, the observer could well think that the engine was by de Winton; the vertical boiler can be seen and the curved crosshead slide-bar has the characteristic de Winton look. On the other hand, the engine has not got the familiar de Winton symmetrical side view. It has side tanks, a feature not usually seen on engines from the Caernarfon company. The author has attempted to analyse the photographs and in doing so, hopes that the reader will forgive the somewhat way-out reasoning.

The first problem is to establish a scale for the photographs, as there is an almost complete lack of reliable reference points. The author has attempted to deduce dimensions by inference and the following calculations are based on "measurements" taken from the photographs. The appended copy photographs are of a smaller scale. On the side view (A), the engine is five and a half "man-widths" long. If "average man" is twenty two inches (508mm) wide, an estimate of the length can be obtained. i.e. 5.5 X 22 inches = 121 inches = **10.1 feet long** (3.1m). Although indistinct, the engine appears to have outside frames.

Referring to the three-quarter view (B); as well as the lack of reliable measurable components, an additional difficulty is the variation of scale due to the oblique viewpoint. If we assume that the distance between the man's knees is 13mm on the photograph and 13 inches (330mm) actual, a horizontal scale of 1mm. = 1 inch (25.4) can be inferred. Applying this scale to the photograph engine length of 116mm, results in an actual length of 116 inches or 9.7 feet (2.9m). The two length calculations average (10.1+9.7)/2 = 9.9 feet, say **10.0 feet** (3.05m). Returning to photograph "B", the length between wheel centres is 66mm. Again, application of the scale 1mm = 1 inch, results in an inferred wheelbase of 66 inches or **five feet six inches** (1.6m).

Similar principles can be used to obtain a vertical scale. On the footplate on photograph "A" there is a boy, who the author estimates to be 5 feet 3 inches tall, i.e. 63 inches (1.600m). On the photograph he is 65mm. tall. A vertical scale would therefore be 63/65 = *0.97mm = 1 inch*. i.e. virtually the same value as the inferred horizontal scale. The boiler is not too clear on either photograph but it would appear to be 4'6" to 5'0" wide. The actual figure cannot be estimated, as the thickness of the lagging is not known.

At this stage it is useful to compare the calculated measurements with known de Winton engines. It has already been stated that the actual measurements are not reliable due to viewpoint anomalies; but the ratio of total length to wheelbase could be less affected by the view-point. The author has calculated from photographs, that the mean length/wheelbase ratio of ten kown "two foot" gauge de Winton engines is **2.42**. The same ratio for *Peris* is **1.82**. Even allowing for the "way-out" method the difference is such, as to suggest, that if *Peris* was a De Winton, it was a significantly different design to other engines from that company.

The Dinorwig Vertical
Boiler Engine "Peris"

Although the gentleman sitting on photograph "A" and the "five and a half men" on photograph "B", mask a lot of detail, it would now seem possible to produce a block side elevation of the engine. Illus.7. As the engine has a vertical cylinder rivetted to the boiler, one of the driving wheel axles must have been vertically below it. The position of the other axle can be determined by using the total length/wheel base ratio. On the photographs the position of the water tanks can be seen. The clearer photograph "B" shows the tank is alongside the boiler and on photograph "A" the positions of a number of the tank rivets are just visible, again alongside the boiler. The word *Peris*, with letters about six inches high, is clearly visible on the photo "B" tank side. If the thickness of the tank is assumed to be eight inches (203mm), it would contain about 65 gallons (295 litre) of water, or 130 gallons (590 litre) if there were two tanks.

The boiler is rather indistinct but appears to have been about six feet (1.83m) high; the actual measurement cannot be estimated as again, the thickness of the lagging is not known. Some pipe work can be seen above the boiler but there is no indication as to whether it was for live or exhaust steam or both. The

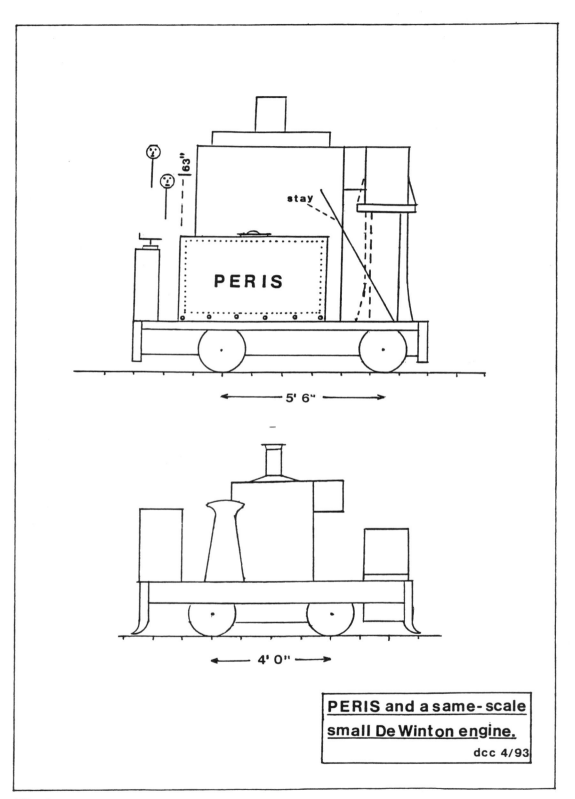

63"

stay

PERIS

5' 6"

4' 0"

PERIS and a same-scale small De Winton engine.

dcc 4/93

Illus.7

The Hunslet response to De Winton

view from both sides shows that there was only one cylinder over the leading axle. There now remains one main item to be located, the coal bunker. There is no obvious sign of this; it could have been on the footplate or in the place of one of the tanks. Unless there was something like a well tank, the one 65 gallon (295 litre) tank would have greatly restricted the range of the engine. Of course, there is always the possibility that the engine had a tender to carry the coal.

It is difficult to ascertain whether the cylinder and valve-gear were rivetted directly to the boiler shell or whether they were supported by the slide-bar assembly or perhaps both. Photograph "A" appears to show the valves and cylinder to be separate from the boiler but photograph "B" suggests that they were rivetted to the boiler shell. If it was the latter, it was a bad practice as the reactive thrust would have tended to twist the shell and open up the rivetted joints. A crosshead slide-bar can be partially seen and, to some extent, it might have supported the cylinder. The provision of the stays is curious, one can be clearly seen on photograph "B" and on close examination of "A", another two are visible. The fact that they are of different lengths suggests that, following operational experience, they were inserted, where there was available space, to counteract a reactive thrust. (It was normal de Winton practice to rivet the cylinders to the boiler shell, either directly or via a support plate.) Some later engines e.g. *Arthur* had the cylinders mounted on a separate assembly; possibly to prevent the difficulties just mentioned. What was the situation on *Wellington*? Unfortunately, nothing is visible, but as the boiler shell was squatter, only about four feet high, would there have been sufficient space to mount the cylinder and valve-gear on the boiler? It seems that there could have been more than one type of vertical boiler engine in use at Dinorwig. Returning to *Wellington*, it has already been demonstrated that in 1895, it performed efficiently, but with such a small boiler, one must question its ability to make sufficient steam for anything but the shortest journey. A water tank can just be seen on the left side of the boiler, but like *Peris*, no coal bunker is visible. There remains the possibility that the name *Wellington* was used by more than one vertical boiler engine.

It was very considerate of the man to sit down and have his photograph taken, as he provides a measure of the wheel diameter. If the space above the wheels is the same as the rail height, the distance between the man's knees and the ground can give an indication of the wheel diameter. i.e. 20 inches (508mm).

Were the engines from de Winton? The author is the first to admit that one cannot really base an assessment on the distance between a man's knees, but there are clearly significant de Winton features in the design. *Wellington* has been shown to have been successful in the quarry and presumably, so were the later *Harriet* and *Peris*. However, the design can only be described as archaic. The photograph has almost certainly come from a recently found collection that also included the 1870 Hunslet engine *Dinorwic*, inferring that the design was pre 1870. H. A. Jones has commented that De Winton were essentially marine engineers, and that their early locomotives were nothing more than a small marine engine mounted on a four-wheel truck. It is said that De Winton only built two single cylinder engines and that they had double flange wheels[42]. Although the photograph is not too clear, there is nothing to suggest that the engine had two cylinders. The wheels appear to be double flanged. As *Harriet* was built before *Peris*, it would surely suggest that it was of similar design. On balance, the author believes that *Peris* and probably *Harriet* did come from de Winton and that there could well have been others. However, they were soon to be outclassed by the arrival from Hunslet of the more advanced and expensive *Dinorwic*. It would seem possible that Dinorwig never had a two-cylinder de Winton; despite the fact that they were widely used in other North Wales quarries. Incidentally, Messrs Hunslet produced a series of vertical boiler locomotives, but they were of a more advanced design than the de Wintons and none are known to have reached Dinorwig.

The gentleman sitting on the running plate of *Peris* has done us a good turn, and the author wonders what he would have thought, had he known that his knees would be the subject of a discussion, more than 100 years later.

'Maid Marian' out of use at Pen Garret. 1965

14. Thomas H. Morris

I first met "Tommi" Morris in 1965. I was making my first visit to Dinorwig Quarry to inspect the redundant engines being offered for sale. There were about six of us, who had been instructed by the Managing Director to report to Mr Morris, the Chief Engineer at his office in the Gilfach Ddu workshops. This was to be the start of a friendship that was to last until he died in 1980.

Our party was initially interested in *Jerry M* and *Cackler*, the two lake level tramway engines. However, Mr Morris advised us to leave them alone; their boilers had seen better days. His recommendation was to consider *Maid Marian* which had recently been withdrawn from service at Pen Garret, 1,460 feet above sea-level. I can remember the long climb to that level; part of it was along the Fox's Path. This was a misnomer, it consisted of 422 steps. Our party was of mixed ages ranging from a teenager to Mr Morris, who at the time, was 65 years old and contemplating retirement. At the bottom of the steps, the younger ones started a brisk climb upwards. I can clearly remember Mr Morris saying, with a smile on his face, "Stick with me, we shall be at the top first." And he was right, before we were half way up, we passed our puffing and panting colleagues. It was a lesson we all learned very quickly. I can also remember that close to the 2,000 feet level, one of our number rather foolishly, asked the whereabouts of the "gents". Mr Morris replied, with that same grin on his face, "Use your imagination, man". He was a man with a gentle but potent sense of humour.

He was born in 1898, the son of a quarryman, and became an apprentice at an early age. Apart from wartime service in the Royal Flying Corps, he spent the whole of his working life in the quarry. He had a reputation for engineering work in dangerous situations, such as anchoring cables to a rock face. Such work necessitated an expert knowledge of the geology of the rock. In 1957 he was appointed Chief Engineer of the Company. The Management were not too keen on visitors; but he was a helpful and understanding man who always found time to have a chat with the genuine enquirer; particularly when it was realised that the days of the steam engine were numbered.

Although he retired in November 1966, he could often be seen chatting to old friends in the quarry, until it closed in 1969. I used to call on him at his home in Caernarfon, where there was always a welcome, particularly if my wife and children were with me. Olwen, his daughter, always served tea and home-made cakes, and there were always apples and oranges for the children. He was always anxious to pass on his knowledge and tales of the quarry. In 1980 he died, survived by his daughter and son John, who also worked at the quarry. He will long be remembered by those fortunate enough to have known him.

By way of a postcript; in 1993 *Maid Marian* still has the boiler recommended by Mr Morris in 1965.

Off to buy an engine.
'Tommy' Morris on left

69

15. Engines on Inclines

In 1966, the author was fortunate to be present when three "Alice" Class engines were lowered down four and a half quarry inclines, from Pen Garret to lake-level; a difference in level of more than 1,000 feet (305m). The three engines were *Rough Pup*, *Bernstein* and *Maid Marian*. It was a major undertaking to lower one engine, but when three, were brought down at the same time, the television turned up for the occasion.

In an earlier chapter the movement of engines on a "tanc" incline has been discussed; but on this occasion, the engines were lowered on their own wheels. In earlier times, they would have been moved in a dismantled state; indeed there was a special waggon for carrying a boiler. Sometimes engines were fitted with double-flange wheels for the journey. A series of photographs is appended and for the sake of continuity *Michael* is included. Before making the descent the engine's springs were packed with wood blocks to improve stability.

The series commences with *Rough Pup* at Pen Garret Illus.8. It will be seen that the chimney and tank have been removed. It was usual to remove the chimney in order to allow the engine to pass under the incline drum, but the reason for removing the tank is not clear. It is shown on a "wagan llwythwr" awaiting a push to the incline top Illus.9. After arrival at the incline, *Bernstein* is seen being manoeuvred under the incline "roller" Illus.10. The next photograph Illus.11 depicts *Bernstein* teetering on the edge, picking up courage prior to taking the plunge over the edge. On the way down we see *Maid Marian* Illus.12 with the "driver" in control of the brake. (I wonder what the factory inspector would have thought? Not a lot). At the bottom of the incline *Bernstein* Illus.13 can be seen, derailed after doing a "shimmy" on its buffer beams. This occurred at the change from the slope to the level, when the wheels lifted off the track. *Michael* Illus.14 can be seen in 1965, complete with chimney and crew of John H. Evans, Ellis Jones and Alun Rowlands, at the bottom of an incline; resting before the next descent. Down at lake level, *Maid Marian* is shown with a now relieved Hugh Jones Illus.15 and finally, the same engine Illus.16 awaits a tow by "No.1" to the workshops.

Mention must be made of the descent of *Alice*, the last engine to be brought down the mountain. *Alice* was last steamed in 1966 at "Australia", although by this time it had become very delapidated. It was not long before the wheels and axles were removed, leaving the remainder of the engine resting on the frames. However, it was still a valuable source of spares, and following purchase by the West Lancashire Light Railway, they managed to lift the wheelless engine on to slate-waggons and lower them down five, more or less derelict, inclines. The whole operation, which had to be carefully planned, took six months to complete. It must be remembered that, all the equipment required had to be man-handled to the site. The author can remember being a member of a small party that carried a small winch up the Fox's Path to Pen Garret; it was a struggle. The work involved in manhandling jacks and lifting gear even higher up the mountain can only be fully appreciated by those who have been to "Australia". In addition, the potentially severe weather conditions at such an exposed site, 1,650 feet (503m) above sea-level, must not be forgotten. It was a truly remarkable feat.

'Rough Pup' August 1966, Pen Garret. Partially dismantled prior to lowering down incline

Illus.8

Illus.9

Dinorwig Quarries Aug.1966
Pen Garret level.
Shed contains partially
dismantled Bernstein,
Maid Marian and Ruston
in space vacated by
'Rough Pup'. 'Rough Pups'
tank on slate waggon

Illus.10

Bernstein at
incline head

Illus.11

Bernstein at
incline head

Maid Marian being
lowered down incline

Illus.13

*Bernstein de-railed
at the foot of incline*

Illus.14

*Michael at incline foot
(from left): John H. Evans,
Ellis Jones, Alun Rowlands*

Illus.15

*Maid Marian at
incline bottom
with Hugh Jones,
Chief Engineer*

Illus.16

*Maid Marian
awaiting a tow
by No.1*

16. From a Notice Board at the Foot of A5 Incline, 1965

Travelling Rules
for Persons Travelling on Inclines

1.   No more than 8 persons shall ride in any one waggon.

2.   No more than 3 waggons shall be coupled together to form a "PASS" or set.

3.   The maximum speed at which waggons carrying men may travel is 5 miles per hour.

4.   The man appointed as Hooker shall use the following code of bell signals for controlling the movement of "passes" on inclines.

One Ring   Stop winding

Two Rings   Start winding

5.   In the event of a derailment, or some other reason, any person riding in a waggon may indicate to the Brakesman and the Hooker that he wishes the "Pass" to be stopped, by raising his arm.

6.   Before the "Pass" is hauled up the incline, the Hooker shall do the following:-

    a) Make sure that each waggon in the "Pass" is securely hooked on to the next and that the safety chains are in position between each waggon.

    b) Make sure that the "Pass" is securely coupled to the hauling rope by means of the main and the safety chains.

    c) When he has made sure that each waggon contains no more than 8 persons, he must warn the occupants that he is about to give the signal to haul up.

7.   No person may stand in a waggon while it is being hauled up an Incline.

8.   Any irregular behaviour by persons travelling on the Inclines shall at once be reported by either the Brakesman or the Hooker to the Overlooker of the Department in which the incline is situated.

Dinorwic Quarry Office

(Not decipherable, probably signed O. T. Williams Managing Director

3rd. July 1959

Sign at bottom of C3 incline

17. The Glan Dinorwig Slate Works

The volume of water running off the Snowdon-Elidir catchment area in to the Afon Peris, must be considerable. After flowing through Llyn Peris and Llyn Padarn it flows under Pont Penllyn (560624) and changes its name to the Afon Rhythallt. At this point the water is at a nominal level of 340 feet (105m) above sea level. After flowing under the bridge, it enters a flat area of reeds and marshland and during wet times, a so called Llyn Bogelyn has formed. Before lifting, the tracks of the L.N.W. and Padarn Railways also passed through the area, about 500 yards (462m) apart, but within half a mile, the valley narrows and at Pont Rhythallt, (545637) the two lines were only 140 yards (130m) apart. At this point the river level had only fallen a few feet. However, within the next 1,00 yards (923m), the two railways closed to 35 yards and by the next bridge, 1,400 yards (129m), the river had fallen to about 300 ft. (92m) above sea level. Such a fall in level of the now sizeable stream would have become a potential and worthwhile power source. Indeed, between the two bridges, there were no less than four leats delivering water to mills at four sites.

By now the reader might be wondering what all this has to do with Dinorwig quarry, but when it is realised that three of the four mills belonged to the Glan Dinorwig Slate Works the connection becomes obvious. The fourth mill was called Faenol and does not feature further in this section. The leat and mill arrangements are shown on the appended Second Edition Ordnance Survey plan. Assuming everything else is equal, the lengths of the three leats give an indication of the relative power available at each site.

A copy of the firm's billhead is included, showing that the concern was established in 1853 and that the proprietor was Samuel Jones. The billhead also shows sketches of three mills in which school writing slates were manufactured. Two of the mills are shown to have overhead final leats and "top shot" water-wheels. The third mill does not show a water-wheel but the plan certainly shows a leat; a smoking chimney can also be seen. In order of power requirement and leat length, the pictures would seem to be in the wrong order. For example, the "sawing and splitting" department would surely be first, followed by "polishing and framing" and "finishing" last. Both the Padarn and L.N.W. railways had sidings on the site, the Padarn delivering raw slate to the "sawing and splitting" works, and the L.N.W.R. removed the finished slates by their siding to the "main line". Excluding the Faenol mill, the Ordnance Survey plan clearly shows leats to at least three, and maybe five water-wheels. The whole site was squeezed in to the narrow area between the two railways. This must have been very inconvenient to work, and to ease transport on the site, the mills were connected by a tramway 563 yards (520m) long. This would almost certainly have been manually or horse worked. Richards[43] writes that the site operated from 1880 to the 1920s, but these dates are not supported by the billhead.

Was there any formal connection with the Vaynol owned Dinorwig quarry? It would seem unlikely. Glan Dinorwig means "bank" or "shore"; the location certainly matches the name and there are at least two ancient "Dinorwig" sites in the near vicinity. It would seem probable that it was an independent concern obtaining its raw material from Dinorwig Quarry.

Are there any remains of the works? What was probably the "sawing and splitting" mill is now an attractive house. However, the mill wheel has been removed and there is no adjacent trace of a leat. Following a battle with the nettles and brambles the author was able to locate other sites. They are now in an advanced state of collapse and covered in creepers and brambles. They are so well camouflaged that finding them can be a matter of luck. The route of the tramway can be located, but when visited by the author in May 1993, it was under water. The L.N.W.R. trackbed, which incidentally, is now gated, was laid on a shallow embankment and the drains underneath are very likely blocked. The longest leat, the one to "sawing and splitting", can be found without too much difficulty. It is now dry, complete with the usual empty paint tins. It was probably blocked when the water-wheel was removed. On a nice day the site is well worth a visit; it must still have some secrets waiting to be found.

After flowing past Faenol Mill, the Afon Rhythallt changes its name, for a second time, to the Afon Seiont, which then flows through Caernarfon harbour to the sea.

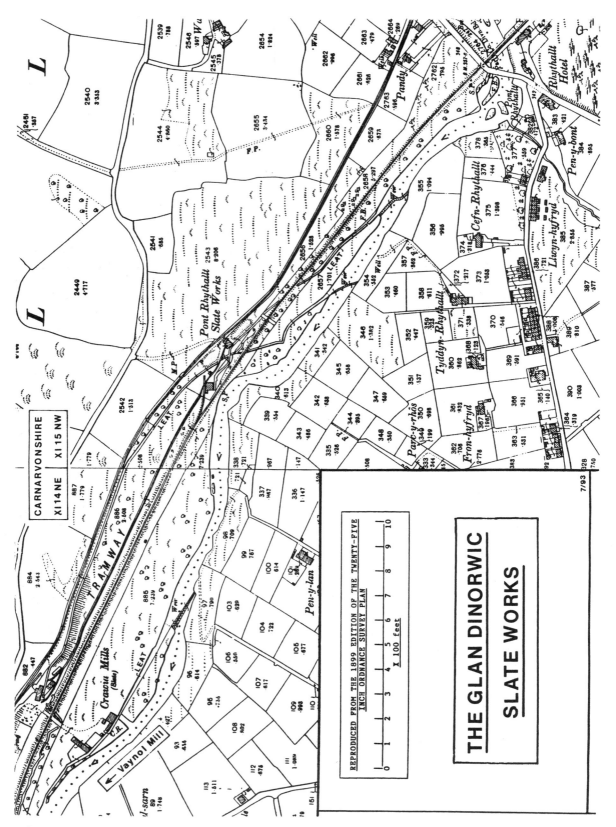

THE GLAN DINORWIC
SLATE WORKS

REPRODUCED FROM THE 1899 EDITION OF THE TWENTY-FIVE
INCH ORDNANCE SURVEY PLAN

X 100 feet

7/93

A surviving Glan Dinorwig mill, now a house. 1993

CONTRACTOR TO H.M. GOVERNMENT

ESTABLISHED 1853.

GLANDINORWIC SLATE WORKS,

Carnarvon, _____ 18__

M _____

SLATE POLISHING DEPARTMENT.   FRAMING & FINISHING DEPARTMENTS   SLATE SAWING & SPLITTING DEPT

Bought of Samuel Jones,

Manufacturer of Framed Unframed & Log Slates,

SOLE MAKER OF THE CELEBRATED "CROWN" SCHOOL SLATES.

Half price allowed for Boxes, if returned carriage paid, & in good order, to Pont Rhythallt Station.

DATE.	DOZENS.	EQUAL IN CASES TO	DESCRIPTION.	SIZE.	PRICE PER DOZEN.	£	S.	D.	£	S.	D.

18. The Dinorwig "Sincs and Ropeways"

Any description of the Dinorwig Quarry transport systems would be incomplete if there was not a mention of the "Blondin" ropeways. In 1859, Charles Blondin, the famous French tight-rope walker, made history by crossing the Niagara Falls on a rope, 160 feet (49m) above the water. He repeated the performance many times, sometimes blind-folded and on other occasions, pushing a wheelbarrow in front of him. He gave his last performance in 1896. Such was his fame, that his name became known in many a high level event or process. Dinorwig Quarry, and similar undertakings elsewhere, utilised a number of high level ropeways and these became known as "Blondins".

Dinorwig is usually considered to be "ponciau" or gallery type of quarry. Other quarries, like Dorothea, were "sinc" types and some of these were several hundred feet deep with near vertical sides. Unless a horizontal tunnel could be dug from the bottom to the outside world, it was necessary to have some form of device to lift out the slate and waste. Although the Garret quarry above "Mills" is usually considered to have been a gallery type; it developed in such a way, that it can be considered to have been a "sinc" type with one side removed. The method of working was certainly similar, and when the diggings had reduced the bottom of the excavation to levels lower than about 1,100 feet (307m), it became a true "sinc". This necessitated the removal of slate and waste by tunnel or "blondin". Both methods were used. A number of tunnels were dug, the lowest of the series being at a level of 1,091 feet a.s.l. (336m). This level, Sinc Twll Clawd started with a tunnel 91 feet (39m) long. It joined the A5 incline at the A5A level. There were other such tunnels. One of these, Bonc Moses, started with a tunnel 210 feet long (65m). After emerging from the tunnel the track went through the Dyffryn triangle, which was also used for turning locomotives. Diesel locomotives operated through some of the tunnels and at least one of them was fitted with electric light signalling.

An examination of known records indicates that there were eleven Blondin systems; there were, no doubt, others. Not all of them worked in to the middle levels of the quarry; some were sited at Twll Mwg on the Lernion level, 1,860 feet a.s.l. They were major constructions. The eleven systems are listed below:

The Dinorwic Aerial Ropeways or "Blondins"

LOCATION	AERIAL ROPE	WINDING ROPE
Sinc Robin	235' x 1 5/8"	550' x 7/8"
Sinc Veronica	240' x 1 5/8"	550' x 7/8"
Princess Vic. No.1	300' x 1 1/2"	550' x 7/8"
Princess Vic. No.2	340' x 1 5/8"	550' x 7/8"
Sinc California	340' x 1 5/8"	660' x 7/8"
Sinc Juliet	260' x 1 5/8"	550' x 7/8"
Abyssinia	340' x 1 5/8"	550' x 7/8"
Twll Dwndyr	300' x 1 5/8"	550' x 7/8"
Penrhydd Bach	340' x 1 5/8"	550' x 7/8"
Twll y Mwg	440' x 1 5/8"	550' x 7/8"
Sinc Vivian	220' x 1 5/8"	550' x 7/8"

In addition to the "blondins" listed above, there were others e.g. Panwys (C7T) 1,810 feet a.s.l. Although the "blondin" was simple, it was an ingenious and effective development of the simple ropeway. Two ropes were used, an aerial rope and a winding rope. The former, the load carrying rope, passed vertically above the loading and landing sites. It sloped down, from the former to the latter, at angles as steep as forty degrees. A multi-wheeled two part trolley could be pulled up and down the aerial rope by means of a winding rope. Immediately above the loading point an adjustable "stop" was clamped to the aerial rope. Reference to the diagram and photographs will help to explain the method of operation. The winding rope which passed over a pulley on the top part was firmly attached to the lower part. When descending the lower part was held in close contact with the top part by means of its own weight. On reaching the "stop", the top part was halted but as the winch was still paying out rope, the two parts separated and the lower part descended to the loading point. After loading, the winding rope was taken in and the load raised vertically. After making contact with the top part, the now combined trolley was hauled up-hill along the aerial rope to the upper discharge polint. At this point, a loop type of restraint or "brake" could be pulled down, by a rope, over the

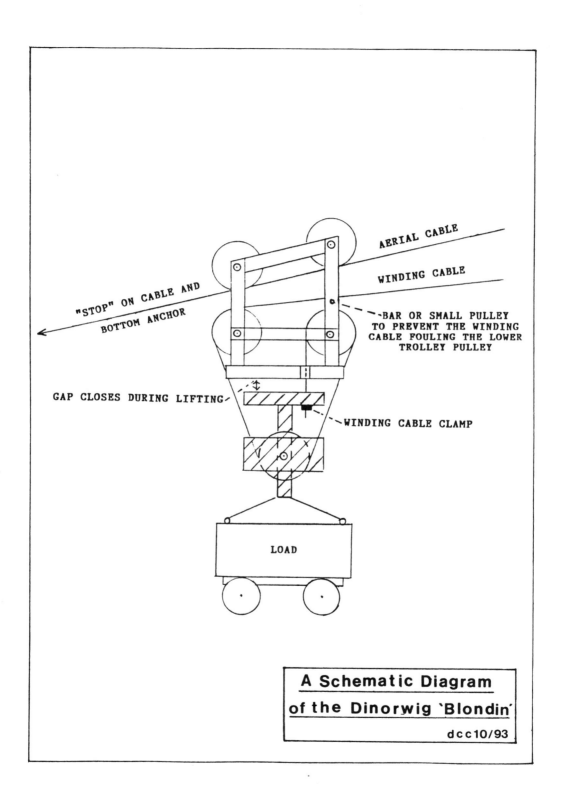

AERIAL CABLE

WINDING CABLE

"STOP" ON CABLE AND
BOTTOM ANCHOR

BAR OR SMALL PULLEY
TO PREVENT THE WINDING
CABLE FOULING THE LOWER
TROLLEY PULLEY

GAP CLOSES DURING LIFTING

WINDING CABLE CLAMP

LOAD

A Schematic Diagram
of the Dinorwig `Blondin`

dcc 10/93

*What the Manager
did not see!*

*A Blondin unloading
point. Note the brake
and the wagons
waiting to be loaded.
Note the brake loop*

upper part, enabling the winding rope to be released and the lower part to fall and release the load. Sufficient head-room had to be provided to permit the separation. The "blondins" were not suitable for universal use. Examination of the diagram and photograph demonstrates that, to ensure that the bottom section remains horizontal, each unit would have been built for use with an aerial rope of pre-determined gradient.

At Dinorwig, towers were built to lift the aerial wire and gain the necessary head room for load handling. Some of the towers were built of steel and others were constructed of slate blocks. The trapezium elevation of these structures was an impressive structure, reminiscent of Brunel's support towers for the Avon Suspension Bridge. The reverse side of the towers were counter-balanced by anchoring the aerial cable in an equally impressive slate block construction.

The rope dimensions table shows that eleven of the winding ropes were the same length, i.e. 550 feet (169m). Can this have been an early attempt to standardise cable lengths? Another problem, worthy of a bit of thought is "How were the cables got to the site? Some cables could have been pulled up on the incline

Two demounted Blondin trolleys. Note that they are
built for a particular cable gradient

rollers, others were not in such convenient locations. As there was a rail connection to winding points, perhaps a precedent was established for the later cable-laying trains on the Llanberis Lake Railway. A working diagram and illustrations are appended.

'Wagan Llwythwr' on incline

19. The Bethel Footbridge

About 300 yards (275m) before a Port bound Padarn Railway train reached the Bethel level-crossing, it passed under a footbridge, known locally as "Charlie Bridge". (From Charles A.S.?) It can still be seen, but the absence of any rails gives it an isolated appearance. There is a rough path from the bridge to a ramshackle, home-made steel plate gate adjacent to a minor road. The bridge was built from scrap rails and iron plates supported by slate block abutments. As the surrounding land is quite flat, there does not seem to be any obvious need for it. It has been said that it was built following the Bethel level crossing accidents. As the first of these did not occur until 1899, it would seem very unlikely, as the bridge is shown on the 1900 edition of the Ordnance Survey map, which was surveyed in 1887-88.

There has long been an air of mystery about the bridge, but the reason for its construction is quite straighforward. Although the railway was built on Faenol property, it crossed a public footpath, and even the mighty Assheton Smith's could not build a railway line across it, without breaking the law. At the time, the path was regularly used by smallholders, and in order to get themselves out of any difficulty, the Faenol built the bridge to carry the footpath over the line. These days, it seems to be little used.

The Bethel Footbridge. 1990

Dolbadarn, Sinc Fawr. 1966

Elidir. 1953

20. Summing Up

Although the previous chapters are, to all intents and purposes, independent of one another, the reader may well have felt that there must be some sort of missing factor or bond between them. For example, the chapters dealing with the puzzling tipping in the lake at Cei Llydan and the 800 foot high tramway along the Domen Fawr. There is also the projected incline from the Allt Ddu-Chwarel Fawr district to Cei Llydan. Is it possible to detect any Grand Plan or strategy?

The philosophy of a lake level route was established in the late 18th. Century, by the slate boats, but the first tramway, the Ellis route of 1824, was established at about the 1,000 level, despite the fact that quarrying was taking place below this level; the processed slate would have to be raised to the new tramway or ferried along the lake. The construction of a line along the route of the later Padarn Railway would certainly have been difficult and expensive although there has been the unsubstantiated hint of such a line in *Canrif y Chwarelwr*[44]. An alternative lake-level route could have been along the south-west shore of Llyn Padarn but this would also have necessitated heavy construction work in Llyn Padarn; although at a later date construction of such a line was undertaken by the L.N.W.R. and opened in 1869. It is unlikely that it ever carried Dinorwig slate, although there were interchange sidings with the Glynrhonwy series of quarries.

Bearing the impediments in mind, it was reasonable to construct the Dinorwig Railway at or near the 1,000 feet level, as at this height it tapped a number of operating quarries. As the lower levels developed the Dinorwig Railway become increasingly irrelevant and following the opening of the Padarn Railway in the early 1840's, it was abandoned in 1843. To a large extent it was replaced by the first version of the uphill "Village Branch" which has been discussed at some length. Mention has also been made of a proposed incline from Allt Ddu to the lakeside at Cae Llydan. A similar scheme was to connect the end of the already constructed 800 feet Domen Fawr tip line by incline to Cei Llydan. If either of these inclines had been built they would have crossed the line of the Spooner survey. If these schemes had been pursued, Cei Llydan would have become a very busy site. It is tempting to speculate that the considerable levelling, filling-in and widening of the track-bed, were the first moves in the provision of sites for sidings, and the other works associated with a slate quarry.

Let us have another look at the Spooner survey; although not in any way detracting from the suggestions made earlier, there does not seem to be any reason why there could not have been a three-way junction on the Allt Wen hillside; one leg being one or both the inclines from Allt Ddu and Domen Fawr, one with the Spooner line and the other to Cei Llydan. Such a system, which would have necessitated a levelled area on the hillside, would have provided a means of getting slate to the lakeside sidings. It would have involved a considerable excavation on the hillside but this would have been child's-play compared with the major civil engineering works in the quarry. An alternative scheme would have been to use the completed section of the Spooner line in reverse; i.e. transporting the slate brought along the then lower Domen Fawr to level A2 on the main incline system. Following a drop by the A2 and A1 inclines or their predecessors, the Gilfach Ddu terminus of the Padarn Railway would have been reached. Many years ago, the author discussed these ideas with the Rev. Herbert Thomas, whose family was descended from the two Griffith Ellis', father and son, both were managers of the quarry. He remembers, as a young child, the great plans being discussed in the family.

The Cei Llydan deviation scheme was commenced before the 1888 First Edition Ordnance Survey and the 1899 Second Edition plan shows that it was still active. It could have been the intention to fill-in the Cei Llydan bay and then establish something that today, we might call a marina; although the author hastens to add, that he has not seen any paper-work or other evidence to support the suggestion. A copy of a Rev. Thomas' sketch map is appended to illustrate the situation. Illus.17. There seems little doubt that the geography of the area could have been very different to that we know today. It now seems that unless some documentary evidence is found, it is unlikely that a full explanation will be found.

We are fortunate that the whole of the Llyn Padarn lakeside was not spoiled. Llanberis and its surroundings are becoming established on the tourist route. The quarry itself, the railway, power station and surroundings are rapidly becoming major tourist attractions.

A pause in the return of Michael to lake level. May 12, 1965

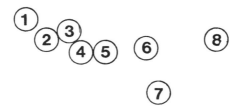

1. Lewis Roberts. Slate loader.
2. Thomas E. Jones. Slate loader.
3. Arfon Jones.
4. John Hughes.
5. Kenneth Jones. Fitter.
6. William John Williams.
7. Alun Roberts.
8. Thomas H. Morris. Chief Engineer.

21. Conclusion

At the beginning of this book it was stated that the interest in slate quarries and Dinorwig in particular, started many years ago. Over the years the author has done a lot of investigation and probing to come up with the facts and theories in this book. They have been written as a series of essays; and that is basically how the book has developed; added to which, are the supporting diagrams and photographs. It has been a fascinating venture and the more one finds, the more one wants to know.

Today, the views across the two lakes are just as striking as they were twenty-five years ago, perhaps more so. It is hard to believe that, when looking across Llyn Peris, one is looking at a world class pumped storage hydro-electric power station; but it is a sobering thought that although the power station is such a colossal undertaking, it is no greater than the quarry was in its hey-day. The row upon rows of galleries are still there. One can still see Wellington Bridge. It is quite probable that a steam engine whistle will be heard. Some of the rock faces have a new appearance but it is only a matter of time before they revert to their old appearance. It is a tribute to the designers that the change in the view is so little. There cannot be many places where a change has contributed so much, so quickly to the economy of a small town. Llanberis used to have a sombre appearance; but now it is bright with many attractions. To remind us of the old days, the old quarry workshops now house the North Wales Slate Museum. Because of the relative isolation of Llanberis, the quarry had to be self-sufficient and some of the old arts are being preserved. Outside an old quarry engine can be seen heading off down the Padarn Railway line on its journey alongside the lake, passing Cei Llydan and on to Penllyn. A now flooded Vivian Quarry is part of an almost complete quarry system with a whole series of inclines; some of them, quite unique in design. A "blondin" has been installed and the old quarry yard is now a car-park. The power station has become a major tourist attraction.

Twenty-five years ago there was uncertainty in the town; today it has become a unique North Wales resort in which the old and new appear to be very closely associated. In such an environment the old quarry and its workers will never be forgotten.

22. Appendix

Calculations Relating to Chwarel Fawr and the "Village" Branch
Based on the "Twenty-five Inch" Ordnance Survey Plan

THE CHWAREL FAWR INCLINE

Length of incline = 3.94 inches
(3.94 x 5,280)/25 = 832 feet (291m)

Height at top of incline (C)	= 942 feet (287m)
Height at bottom of incline (D)	= 800 feet (244m)
Difference	= **142** feet (43m)
Gradient = 832/142	= **1 in 5.9** (16.9%)
Records quote a figure of	= **1 in 6.0 (16.7%)**
Top of Chwarel Fawr pit (E)	= **961 feet (293m)**
Bottom of Chwarel Fawr pit (D)	= **800 feet (244m)**
Depth of pit	= **161** feet (49m)
Length of tunnel on map (25″)	= 2.72 inches (69mm)
(2.72 x 5,280)/25	= **574** feet (175m)

BONC BACH LEVEL

On incline, from bottom to B-B wharf	= 1.10 inches (28mm)
Height difference, top to bottom	= 142 feet (43mm)
Full length of incline on map	= 3.95 inches (100mm)
100 mm is equivalent to 142 feet	
28 mm is equivalent to (142/100) x 28	= **39.8** feet
Level of Bonc Bach = 800 + 40	= **840** feet
Length of Bonc Bach tunnel – 33mm	= 1.22 inches
(1.22 x 5,280)/25	= **258** feet

POSSIBLE TOP LEVEL IN CHWAREL FAWR

On 25″ Plan, Ellis incline = 60 mm long

Height at top = (959 + 948)/2	= 954 feet (291m)
Height at bottom	= 895 feet (273m)
60 mm equ. (945 - 895)	= **59** feet (18.0m)
23 mm = (59x23)/60	= **22** feet (6.7m)
Height of level = (954-22)	= **932** feet (284m)

THE "CHWAREL FAWR" INCLINE REPLACEMENT TRAMWAY

(associated with the engine worked "village" branch)

Length of tramway on 25″ Plan	= 16 x 10 mm increments
	= 160 mm = **6.3″**
Length of tramway = (6.3 x 5,280)/25	= **1,331** feet (406m)
Rise = 942-895	= **47 feet** (17.7m)

Gradient = 1,331/47 = **1 in 28.0** (3.8%)

THE "VILLAGE BRANCH TRAMWAY
THE HORSE WORKED TRAMWAY (F-G1)

Length of tramway on 25″ Plan = 21.3 x 10mm increments
= 213mm = **8.4″**

(8.4x5280)/25 = **1,774 feet** (541m)

Rise = (1,000-942) = **58 feet** (17.7m)

Gradient = 1,774/58 = **1 in 31** (5.6%)

Radius of curve at the bottom of the branch on the 25″ plan
= 5mm = 0.2″. Radius on the ground = (0.2/25)x5,280 = 42 feet
= **14 yards** = **0.6 chains** (12.8m)

THE GRADIENT OF THE STEEPEST PART OF THE HORSE WORKED LINE

(This has been calculated by using the even graded engine worked line as a datum)

The steepest section = 85 mms = 3.3″ on the 25″ Plan.

Length of steepest section = (3.3 x 5,280)/25 = **697** feet = (213m)

At 697 feet there has been 22.5 feet rise on the constant grade   engine route.

Gradient on horse route = 697/(22.5+x). (x = height of horse route above engine route), x = 12 feet. (3.7m)

Therefore max. gradient = 697/(22.5+12) = 697/34.5 - **1 in 20** = (5%)

THE ENGINE WORKED TRAMWAY

Length of tramway on 25″ Plan = 23.2 x 10mm steps
= 232 mm = **9.1″**

(9.1 x 5,280)/25 = **1,922 feet** (608m)

Rise = (1,600-942) = **58 feet** (17.7m)

Gradient = 1,922/58 = **1 in 33** (3.0%)

Top of C5 incline (Australia). Note overbridge on right
carrying 'mainline'

Bernstein (F) Maid Marian (R) View over Maid Marian boiler

Velinheli in Gilfach Ddu workshop following withdrawal

23. Bibliography (In alphabetical order of authors)

	Chronicles of a Caernarfon Ironworks (De Winton). R. Abbott, CHS 17.
	Maid Marian's Century. G. Barnes. Llanuwchllyn Ex. No.52.
	Stone Blocks and Iron Rails. B. Baxter. David and Charles 1966.
	Old Copper Mines of Snowdonia. D. Bick. 1982. Pound House, Newent.
BOYD FR2	*The Festiniog Railway.* Vol.2. J.I.C. Boyd. 1975 Oakwood.
BOYD NC2	*Narrow Gauge Railways in North Caernarvonshire.* Vol.2. J.I.C. Boyd. Penrhyn Railway. 1985 Oakwood.
BOYD NC3	*Narrow Gauge Railways in North Caernarvonshire.* Vol.3. J.I.C. Boyd. Dinorwic Quarry and Railways. 1986.
	On the Welsh Narrow Gauge. J.I.C. Boyd. Brad. Barton. *(a picture book)*
	Industrial and Independent Locomotives and Railways of North Wales. Pkt. Book F.V. Bradley. 1968. BLC/ILS
	Camb. Univ. Dir. of Aerial Photography, various. 20/7/48, 24/7/49, 20/7/63.
CHS	*Transactions of Caernarvonshire Historical Society.*
	Slates to Velinheli. D.C. Carrington. Stephenson Loco. Socy. 10,11,12,/1972.
	Enlarged reprint of above. D.C. Carrington & T.F. Rushworth. 1976. Maid Marian Loco. Fund.
	Updated version of above. 1993. Bala Lake R.S. Colour photo. covers.
	The North Wales Hydro-Electric Power Stations North West Region. C.E.G.B.
	Chwareli y Chwarelwr 1974. G.A.S.
	"Snowdonia". G. Embleton. Comment. of O.S. 1″ Sheet 107. 1969. Geographical Association.
	Cambrian Coasters. R. Fenton. 1989. World Ship. Socy.
GAS	*Caernarvonshire Record Office/Gwynedd Archives Service*
	Canrif y Chwarelwr. Emyr Jones. 1963 Gwasg Gee.
	Bargen Dinorwig. Emyr Jones. 1980 Tŷ ar y Graig.
	Felinheli. R. Chambers Jones. 1992 Bridge Books.
	The North Wales Quarrymen 1874-1922. R.M. Jones 1982 University of Wales Press.
	Griffith Jones. (P. Dinorwic photographer) 1980 G.A.S.
	Narrow Gauge Railways in North Wales. C. Lee 1945. Railway Publishing Co. Ltd.
	The Slate Quarries of North Wales in 1873. ed. M.J.T. Lewis. 1987. Snowdonia Nat. Park.
	Llechi-Slate. ed. M.J.T. Lewis. G.A.S. *(a picturebook)*
LIND	*A History of the North Wales Slate Industry.* J. Lindsay. 1974. David and Charles.
	Dinorwig Village Loco. Shed. A. McDougall 1982. Llanuwchllyn Express. Summer 1982.
	Royal Air Force. . . . Dept./Env. F22 82 RAF 908.
	Industrial Archaeology of Wales. D. Morgan Rees. 1975. David and Charles.
	A Gazeteer of the Welsh Slate Industry. A. Richards. 1991. Gwasg Carreg Gwalch.
	Farming in Caernarvonshire. R.O. Roberts. 1973. CRO
	The Grand National. Vian Smith. 1969. Stanley Paul.
	The Padarn and Penrhyn Railways. S. Turner. 1975. David and Charles.
	Steam Coasters and Short Sea Traders. C.V. Waine. 1980. Waine Research.
	Three Stops to the Summit. R. Williams. 1990. Cyhoeddiadau Mei. Refs. to A.S. family.
	Groby and its Railways. D.A. Ramsey, 1982. TEE Publishing. 216 Coventry Rd. Hinckley, Leics.
	The Slate Industry. Merfyn Williams. 1991. Shire Publications.

24. References

1. GAS 4190
2. Harley p.9.
3. GAS . . . ?
4. LIND. p.56 and on.
5. BOYD NC3 p.3 and on.
6. Richards p.236
7. (GAS "Maritime Wales" No.4. 7/1979.
   (CHS Transactions No.40. p.87
8. CHS Transactions No.21. p.138.
9. "Countess" is a size of slate. 20"x12".
10. LIND p.61.
11. BOYD NC3 p.7.
12. BOYD NC3 p.26.
13. Reminiscences of the late Thomas Assheton Smith. (picture).
14. LIND p.61.
15. BOYD NC2 p.9.
16. BOYD NC3 p.42.
17. Bradley. Private communication.
18. BOYD FR2 p.578.
19. Rev. H. Thomas. Private Communication.
20. Bargen Dinorwig. p.78. Emyr Jones.
21. C.E.G.B. N.W. Region. North Wales.
    Hydro-electric Power Stations. (undated)
22. Bargen Dinorwig. Emyr Jones. p.75.
23. H.R. Jones. Private Communication.
24. GAS "Griffith Jones" 1980. Photos of Port Dinorwig reconstruction.
25. "Llanuwchllyn Express" No.52.
26. Padarn and Penrhyn Railways p.154. S. Turner.
27. Rev. Thomas. Private Communication.
28. GAS No. DQ 3250.
29. Quarry stocklist.
30. Slates to Velinheli. p.15.
31. GAS No. DQ 3094.
32. Bargen Dinorwig. p.37. Emyr Jones.
33. The Story of Sunderland Point. H. Cunliffe.
34. Railway Mag. 8/1974. K. Jaggers.
35. GAS "Griffith Jones" Photo of yacht AMALTHAE.
36. BOYD NC3 p.42.
37. Railway Mag. 9/1974. p.449. K. Jaggers.
38. BOYD NC3 p.43.
39. BOYD NC3 p.106.
40. Railway Mag. 8/1974. K. Jaggerrs.
41. BOYD NC3 Plate No. XCIV.
42. CHS Transactions. Vol.17. pps. 86-94. R.A.S. Abbott.
    The De Winton Locomotive. R.A.S. Abbott.
43. A Gazateer of the Welsh Slate industry. 1991. A.J. Richards.
44. Emyr Jones. Private communication.
45. BOYD NC3 Plate No. XCVI.

Holy War, Penrhydd Bach. 1987